CONTENTS

POPULAR PRESS

ABC of electricity

Electricity is the source of energy for heating, lighting and powering many appliances in your home. In knowing all about it, you can tackle all sorts of repairing and fitting jobs safely.

Rather like the water supply, electricity comes into most homes from some unknown outside source: but how does it arrive and what is it? Pushing down a switch gives immediate light and power to drive fans, cleaners and kitchen equipment; it also provides gradually increasing heat in kettles, cookers, fires, immersion heaters and central heating. But beyond this point electricity is to most people a mystery, and to many something to be feared. Some people even think that electricity leaks out of every power socket without a plug in it, or lamp-holder that does not have a bulb in it. An understanding of the simple principles of how electricity works can help to remove the fear.

Although it may help you to understand electricity by comparing it with the water supply, it is important to remember that this is only an analogy; the electricity supply is in some ways similar to the water supply, but it is quite wrong to suppose it will continue to behave like water in every respect. Electricity will only flow in a conductor; you can compare this to water flowing in a pipe. But while water will keep flowing out of a broken pipe, electricity will not continue flowing out of a broken wire unless there is some other conductor – a screw-driver, a hacksaw blade, some other metal or wet material – to conduct it away. The reason is that electricity does not really 'flow', it is much more like the hydraulic fluid that operates the brakes of a car or the big jacks used in constructional engineering.

Hydraulic fluid transmits pressure along a pipe from one place to another (**see 1**); and if the pipe is cracked, or there is not enough fluid, the system will not work. In the same way, electricity supplied to the home at a certain 'pressure' is used to do the work of driving motors, or making heat and light.

The earth will conduct electricity very easily. The human body will not conduct it so easily, but easily enough. If you touch the bare end of a 'live' wire, or the contacts in a lamp-holder when the switch is on, the electricity will be conducted through your body to the earth. If you are lucky, the electricity will make your arm muscles jerk away as soon as you touch the wire, and you will only suffer an electric 'shock'. If you are unlucky, the electricity will make your finger muscles clamp onto the wire so that you cannot let go. You may die by electrocution or at the least be badly burned and anyone who tries to help you by touching you will suffer the same. In this situation the helper must switch off the electricity or, failing this, try sharply jerking the afflicted person away with a rope, tea towel or scarf, or anything non-conducting (that is, not metal or a wet material) like a broom.

DC or AC

Electricity can be supplied in two ways in domestic circumstances: as direct current (DC) or as alternating current (AC). All batteries – the lead battery

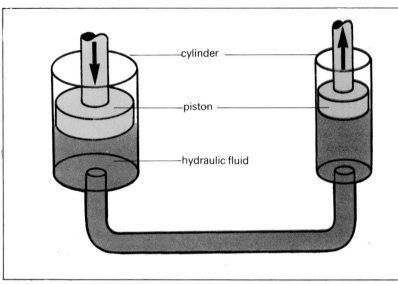

of a car, the 'dry cell' of an electric torch or transistor radio, or the rechargeable battery of certain pieces of portable electronic equipment – supply DC. So do many private domestic generators, such as used to be installed in houses and farms far away from public supplies. The national electricity grid now provides AC supply to all but the most remote areas of Great Britain. Light bulbs and simple heaters will work equally well on DC or AC supply, but most modern electrical equipment is made to operate on AC only, and needs special modification for DC supply.

Voltage This term denotes the pressure exerted by the electricity supply. So a torch battery, at 1.5 volts, will give you no more than a tiny tingle if you put your wet tongue across the contacts; but don't try the same thing with your home supply at 240 volts!

It is easy to understand how the electricity from a DC source such as a battery can be imagined as exerting this pressure; but what about AC? In an AC supply the 'direction of flow' of electricity changes backwards and forwards, usually 50 times every second. The 'mains supply' enters your home as two wires: a 'live' wire (L) at a pressure of 240 volts, and a 'neutral' wire (N), which is connected to the earth. The live wire is coloured red and the neutral wire black.

The 'earth' wire

Why, then, is there a separate earth wire inside the home? The reason is that the neutral wire is only conducting to earth while everything is working properly. If a live wire works loose, or its insulation is worn away, it may touch the outside casing of an appliance; this is why any metal part of an appliance that can be touched, switch plates, lamp-holders etc. should be independently connected directly to earth by means of the earth wire.

Current and resistance

To understand a little more about electric current, you have to go back to comparing it with water flowing in a pipe (**see 2**). Suppose there is a pump A, which drives water through the pipe B. The system will only work if there is a complete circuit back to A. The pump A can be thought of as the electricity source, and it will only drive the turbine D if the tap C is open. So C is equivalent to a switch in an electrical circuit, and D is any appliance put into the circuit (see 3).

The flow of the water round the pipe circuit is like the 'flow' of electricity in an electrical circuit. As more water per second flows through D, so it will do more work. In the same way, the greater the quantity of electricity flowing each second in the circuit, the more work it will do. The quantity of electricity per second, called current, is expressed in amperes (or amps for short). But here, once again, you must remember that electricity is not really like water. For instance, if you consider the statement 'more water is flowing per second', you think of it as flowing faster; but electricity always 'flows' at the same speed, and it is the amount of work it is capable of doing that changes. Imagine instead that the water is always flowing at the same pressure and the same speed, but being pumped through pipes of bigger bore.

You can also see that if the pipes were made narrower, it would become more and more difficult to get the water to flow, until eventually the pipe was so narrow that the pressure would not be sufficient to drive the water through at all. The narrow bore of the pipe is therefore exerting resistance. In the same way, part of an electrical circuit can be a resistance. In passing this resistance, the electricity does work. The work may consist of driving a motor or be in the form of heat or light. If there is no resistance to the electric current, electricity will flow through the circuit in such quantity that it is as if a pipe has burst: it can (almost literally) 'drain' the supply. This is why fuses are put into every part of the home electricity supply. If there is a 'short circuit', the large current flowing through the thin wire of the fuse heats it up and causes it to melt – breaking the circuit and stopping the flow.

Volts, amperes, ohms and watts

Resistance is measured in ohms. The relationship between volts, amperes and ohms is very easily expressed: volts = amperes × ohms.

As the domestic AC supply is at about 240 volts, and the safety limit for ordinary appliances is set at 13amps, you can calculate that the minimum resistance a circuit can offer is about 18 ohms.

The work that the electricity does is measured in watts. If you look at the manufacturer's plate on any electric appliance (see 4) you will see that it is rated at so many volts (220–240 volts, AC 50 cycles) and so many watts. The relationship between watts, volts and amperes is: volts × amperes = watts.

The pressure of the electricity supply – its voltage – does not normally change. The working appliance consumes electricity at a fixed rate. If the domestic supply is at 240 volts, and the appliance is rated at 960 watts, it will be consuming current at the rate of 4amps, which is within safe limits. If the total 'load' of appliances on any one domestic circuit adds up to more than 7200 watts, the current will exceed 30amps and the consumer unit fuse may 'blow'.

One thousand watts equal one kilowatt (kW) and electricity consumed over a period of one hour is called a kilowatt-hour (kWh), or one 'unit' of electricity. Electrical consumption is measured and charged for on this basis.

2

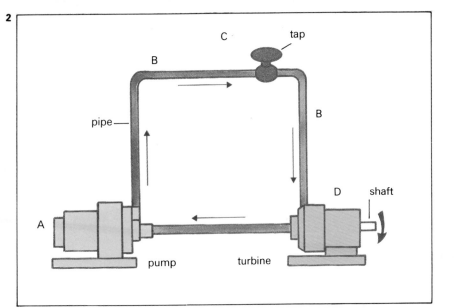

3

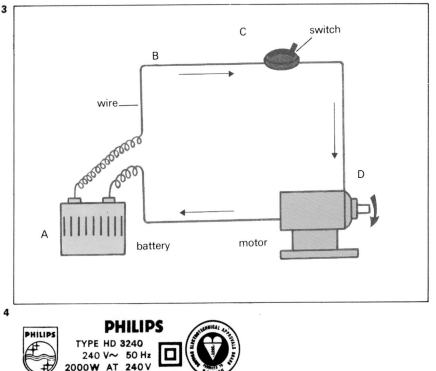

4

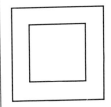

PHILIPS
TYPE HD 3240
240 V~ 50 Hz
2000W AT 240 V
MADE IN GT. BRITAIN

Earthing

When rewiring a plug make absolutely sure the earth wire (yellow/green or green) is properly connected. If it is not you run the risk of an electric shock should the metal casing of an appliance become accidentally live.

The only appliances which do not need earthing are double insulated ones supplied with two core flex and mains operated shavers which are intended for use with special shaver sockets.

Left symbol for double insulation

Source of supply

The main electricity supply enters your home via an underground cable and normally appears at ground level; the system shown here is typical of many homes. On the left is the consumer unit (with a transformer underneath for the front door bell). To the right of the consumer unit is the black meter, which shows the consumption of electricity, and next to that is the sealed unit containing the Electricity Board fuse

When you turn on a switch you naturally expect the light to come on or a particular appliance to work. Circuits feed electricity all round the home, so you can use the power just where and when you want it.

Electricity is generated at a power station and conveyed across country by either underground cables or overhead cables strung between tall pylons. Its voltage is reduced by an enclosed transformer or sub-station in your locality and from there electricity is fed to your home at 240 volts.

Main supply

Cables which conduct electricity from the transformer to the consumer consist of insulated live (red) and neutral (black) conductors protected by an earthed metal sheath. The underground cable terminates in the house at ground level; in districts where there is overhead distribution, the supply is fed into the top of the house through a porcelain tube under the eaves.

In both cases the main supply cable terminates in a sealed unit which holds the service fuse. This fuse is designed to blow if there is a serious fault in the house which has failed to blow the fuse in the consumer unit (or fuse box), thus preventing the supply to neighbouring homes being affected. A 60 or 100amp fuse is connected to the live feed and the neutral conductor is connected to a brass terminal. There is another terminal on the outside of the sealed unit to which the household earth connection is made. The sealed unit containing the fuse belongs to the Electricity Board and must never be opened by the consumer; if the fuse does blow, you should call in the Electricity Board.

Two cables run from the service fuse to the meter, which measures the amount of electricity used. The meter is also the property of the Electricity Board and should never be tampered with by the consumer. The installation from the meter onwards is the consumer's responsibility and includes the two leads from the meter to the consumer unit.

Consumer unit

This contains a main switch and circuit fuses for the whole installation. Most houses have a lighting circuit for each floor so the whole house is not plunged into darkness in the event of a fuse blowing. A high wattage fixed appliance such as a cooker or immersion heater has its own sub-circuit. The cooker is wired directly to its own control switch – into which can be incorporated a power plug for use with other electrical kitchen gadgets. The control switch must be within two metres (or six feet) of the cooker, but separate from it. Make sure you have a long enough lead to the box so you can move the cooker out when cleaning.

Ring circuit

Socket outlets and small fixed appliances such as wall heaters and extractor fans are connected to a ring circuit, formed by a cable comprising a live (red) wire, a neutral (black) wire and a bare earth wire (covered in green/yellow PVC sleeving where it leaves the sheath). The cable used in domestic ring mains is 2.5sq mm twin core and earth, sheathed in PVC. This cable runs from a 30amp fuse in the consumer unit, serves each outlet and returns to the fuse, forming a ring.

The total load for a ring circuit is 30amps (7200 watts). So although it is possible to have an unlimited number of socket outlets on a ring, it is unlikely the number of domestic appliances being used at one time will exceed 30amps. If the circuit were overloaded, the 30amp fuse would blow and therefore maintain the safety requirements. However it is advisable to have a ring circuit for each floor in the house. If the kitchen has a large number of electrical appliances and/or a freezer, you should have a separate ring circuit in the kitchen to prevent overloading and ensure the freezer is not affected by a fault elsewhere.

Plugs used on a ring circuit have square pins and are fitted with 3 or 13amp fuses. The 3amp fuse covers all appliances up to a loading of 720 watts, which includes small appliances such as lamps. A 13amp fuse takes up to 3000 watts.

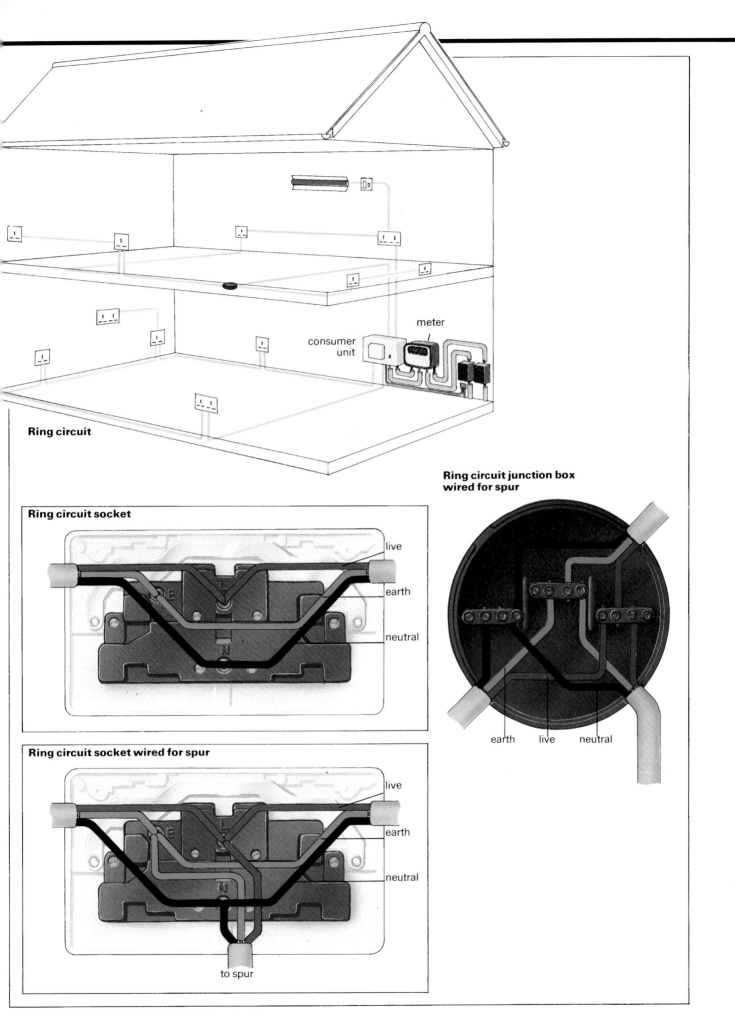

Ring circuit

meter

consumer
unit

**Ring circuit junction box
wired for spur**

earth   live   neutral

Ring circuit socket

live

earth

neutral

Ring circuit socket wired for spur

live

earth

neutral

to spur

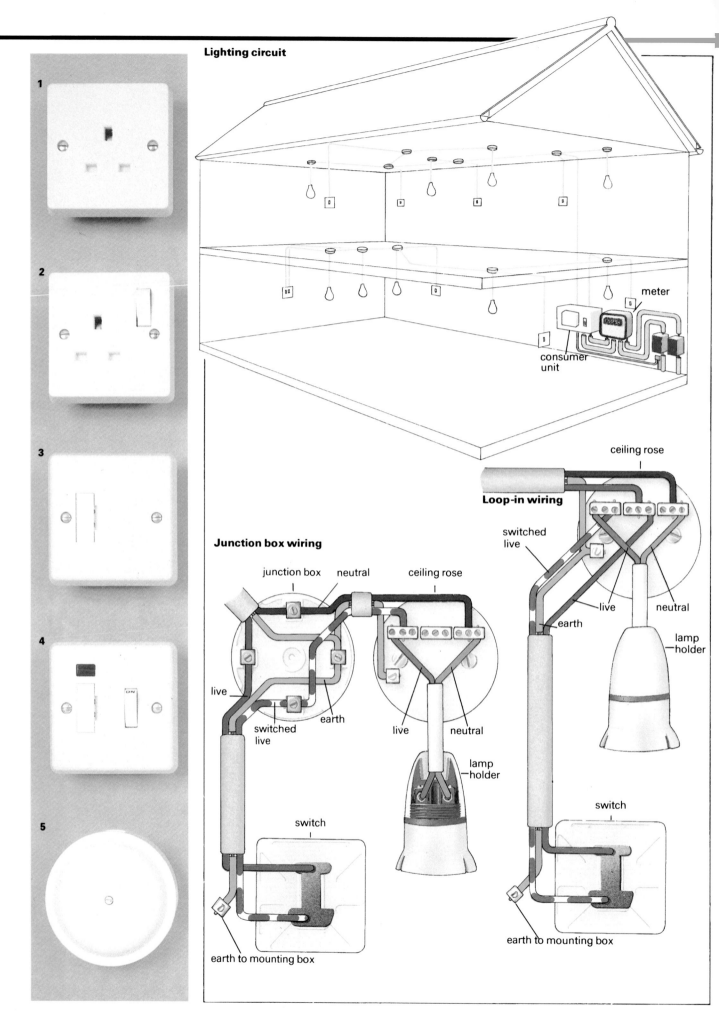

Lighting circuit

meter

consumer unit

Loop-in wiring

ceiling rose

switched live

live

neutral

earth

lamp holder

switch

earth to mounting box

Junction box wiring

junction box

neutral

ceiling rose

live

earth

switched live

live

neutral

lamp holder

switch

earth to mounting box

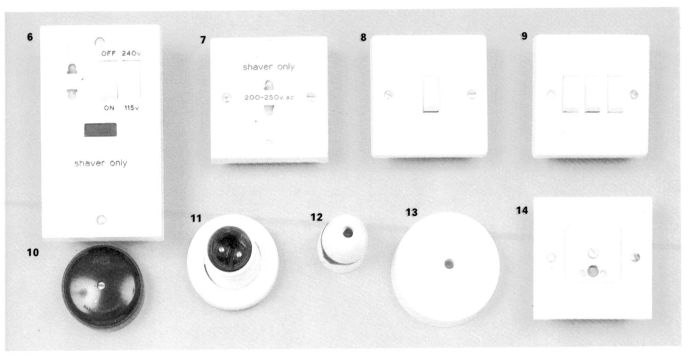

Additional socket outlets may be connected to a ring circuit, but the area served by the circuit should not exceed 100sq m (or 120sq yd).

Non-fused spur extensions

You can connect non-fused spur extensions to the circuit so long as each spur supplies just one single socket outlet, one double outlet or one fixed appliance. The total number of spurs must not exceed the number of socket outlets on the ring main. Only one spur may be connected from each outlet on the ring; for this purpose a junction box wired into the ring is classified as an outlet.

Fused connection units

These outlets, also used on a ring circuit, have the same fuse rating as plugs and are connected to a fixed appliance by a cable or flex. The unit may be switched or unswitched and fitted with an indicator light to show when the supply is connected to the outgoing flex or cable. Like socket outlets, the units can be flush or surface-mounted.

Flex outlets are simply a means of converting from a cable to a flex. A fused, switched connection unit, for example, outside a bathroom may supply a cable leading into the bathroom to feed a wall-mounted heater. Adjacent to the heater would be an outlet to feed the flex into the heater.

The clock connector is a similar type of unit, with a fuse fitted in a special plug into which the flex runs. The plug is retained in the socket by a knurled thumbscrew. Though called a clock connector, this is also suitable for small appliances such as window and wall extractor units.

Lighting circuits

Although lighting circuits are separate from the ring main or power circuit, there is nothing to prevent an individual light being taken from the ring. However, every home should have at least two lighting circuits protected by 5amp fuses. A 5amp fuse will carry up to twelve 100 watt lamps and it is usual, for example in a two-storey house, to plan one circuit for downstairs and another for

upstairs. This will provide enough lighting points for decorative effects as well as general illumination.

Shaver units may also be connected to lighting circuits. For use in a bathroom, or room containing a shower, you must buy a unit which incorporates an isolating transformer. Here the socket is isolated from earth to remove the risk of an electric shock.

Lighting cable

Unlike the ring circuit, lighting cable does not return to the consumer unit. The cable now used is a 1sq mm PVC twin core and earth rated for up to 12amps. It is made up of a red insulated core for live, black insulated core for neutral and a bare earth conductor between them. The three conductors are laid side by side, surrounded by a PVC sheath.

The lighting cable travels from the consumer unit to a series of lighting points for ceiling roses or wall light fittings. It also connects to the switch or switches controlling the lamps and must do this in such a way that the individual switch, unless planned otherwise, does not affect other lights.

Two systems

There are two methods of wiring lights – by junction box or the loop-in ceiling rose. With the junction box system, cable is taken to a series of up to ten junction boxes. These are generally sited between ceiling joists or under floorboards close to where the cable is chanelled under the wall plaster to the switch. The loop-in system is more widely used and the ceiling rose incorporates the function of the junction box.

Extra lighting points may be added to an existing system by connecting cable from the junction box or ceiling rose to the new lighting point and switch.

Lamps may be controlled by switches in more than one place in a house – switches on the ground floor and first floor can both control a half-way or landing light. Or two lamps at different places – possibly in a large room – could be controlled by a double switch.

Cables and flexes

Cables and flex run all round your home – and it's important to know what each is for to make sure you use the right one for the right job.

Cable and flex are probably two of the most misused words when talking about electricity since, contrary to popular belief, they are not interchangeable. Cable is the main wiring carrying the supply to the many outlets in the home; flex is wiring that, for example, connects a lamp-holder to a ceiling rose or a vacuum cleaner to a socket.

Cables

Cables are not normally handled by the domestic consumer, since they have usually been built into the fabric of the house and make up the permanent wiring. Unlike flexes they are seldom moved during their working life; the expensive fine-wire construction of flex is not needed and many cables have single strand conductors running through them.

Cables connect the household electricity supply to flexes through suitable connection boxes such as ceiling roses or socket outlets. There are regulations to ensure cables are supported by clips at specific intervals depending on whether they run vertically or horizontally. PVC sheathed cable, for instance, can be buried in wall plaster without further protection.

Warning Cable should never be laid in grooves cut into joists because of the danger of floorboard nails penetrating the cable. It should pass through holes drilled at least 50mm (2in) below the tops of the joists.

Colour coding has not changed on cables. Red is live, black is neutral and green is earth, although in some types of domestic cable a bare uninsulated wire is the earth. Interior house cable can be single core (one conductor), twin core, twin core and earth, or three core and earth.

If there is a bare earth when cable is attached to a domestic connection box it should be covered with a short length of green PVC sleeving to insulate and identify it.

In some older houses you could well find the cable made up with a number of strands. This cable usually runs in metal conduit which acts as an earth conductor. In modern homes you will also find cable with conductors made of up to seven strands. This is for circuits which carry heavy current, such as for cookers. All modern cable has an outer covering of PVC which is proof against moisture and most common chemicals and acids so it can be safely buried in walls.

Below A selection of cables and flexes used for different installations in the home
1 Single core double-insulated cable
2 Twin core single-insulated cable
3 Twin core double-insulated cable
4 Twin core and earth double-insulated cable
5 Three core and earth cable
6 Twin core and earth double-insulated cable (conductors made up of seven copper strands)
7 Cooper-sheathed twin core cable insulated with chalk lining

1   2   3   4   5   6   7

Flexes

8 Cloth-covered and rubber-insulated three core flex with old colour coding
9 Same flex with new coding
10 Rubber-covered and insulated flex with old colour coding
11 Same flex with new colour coding
12 PVC-covered and insulated three core flex with new colour coding
13 Same flex with old colour coding
14 Unearthed PVC-covered and insulated twin core flex with new colour coding

Flex – or flexible cord – is a conductor of electricity which can be twisted and bent many times without breaking. It comprises metal conductors, each of which is made up of many strands of fine wire (rather than one thick one) encased in plastic or rubber. The finer the strands, the stronger the flex.

Flexes receive a lot of wear and tear, so it is very important they are connected properly and securely. In the case of a plug, the anchorage points must be secure enough to ensure any strain on the flex is taken by the tough outer covering (usually plastic or rubber) and not the metal conductors and the plug terminals. Similarly, connections to appliances must be through equally secure anchorage points to prevent strain at that end of the flex.

If the flex has to be lengthened at any time, it must be connected to another flex of the same type and joined by a proper connector.

Colour coding

Perhaps the most misunderstood aspect of flexes is the international colour code used for the PVC insulating covering. By law the three core flexes – whether sold separately or with an appliance – must have insulation coloured brown for the live wire, blue for the neutral wire and green-and-yellow bands for the earth. On older appliances you may find the live wire is red, the neutral black and the earth yellow.

There are, surprisingly, no regulations as yet covering two core flexes. You may buy an appliance with, for example, black and white plastic covering and no explanation about which is live and which is neutral. The reason is that here it does not matter which wire is connected to which plug terminal. Table and standard lamps are examples where, in most cases, plain two core flex can be used.

Different ratings

There are many variations in the types of flex and cables, although most have special uses in industry. For the domestic consumer flexes vary little. Cables are more varied; there are, for example, special cables with extra protection for outside lighting and garden use.

Cables and flexes are given a rating based on the area of the conductor's cross-section and are described by this area when ordered from a supplier. A cable for a ring circuit, for example, is described as 2.5sq mm (or $2.5mm^2$), representing the cross-sectional area of one of the conductors available for carrying the current. The other conductor carries the same current but in the opposite direction. The earth conductor is slightly smaller than the other conductors in the cable and carries current only when there is a fault.

Changing conditions Cable and flex ratings do vary according to installation conditions, but this is unlikely to affect the domestic consumer. In a very hot situation, such as in an industrial process, a cable could be rated much lower than a similar cable in a domestic location because the rating is based on the rise in temperature that occurs when a conductor carries a given amount of current.

8 **9** **10** **11** **12** **13** **14**

Stripping cable & flex

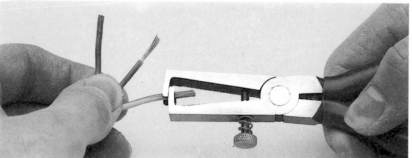

1 Cut carefully along the length of the flex with a sharp knife.
2 Use wire strippers to remove the sheathing and expose the insulated cores
3 Twist the wires together with your fingers
4 After stripping the insulation from cable, slip a length of PVC sleeving over the earth wire
5 On heavy cable, twist the conductors together with pliers

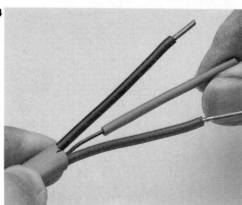

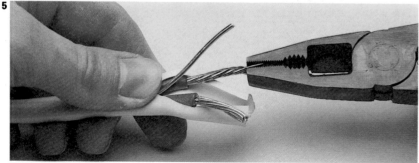

There are certain basic rules you must remember before you start to strip flex or cable for connecting to a plug or appliance or for wiring power or lighting circuits.
● Remove only sufficient insulation to enable the cores to be connected to the terminals; none of the bared wires should be exposed.
● Don't stretch the insulation when stripping or you will weaken the portion remaining on the conductor.
● Take care not to cut through the insulation of conductors, or through a conductor itself, or you will have to shorten the flex or cable and start again. If you damage a conductor the effective current capacity will be lowered and this could cause overheating. Current capacity will also be reduced if you sever any of the fine strands in a length of flex.

Stripping flex
The two most commonly used flexible cords are circular sheathed and braided circular flex. A third, now largely replaced by circular sheathed flex, is twisted twin non-sheath flex.
Circular sheathed Measure the length of sheathing to be removed and carefully run a knife round the sheath, making sure not to damage the core insulation. From this point, make a cut along the length of the flex to the end, cutting through to the inner insulation. Remove the sheathing with pliers, leaving the insulated cores exposed. Measure the length of insulation to be removed from each core and carefully take it off with wire strippers. Always twist the bared ends of each core together to ensure there will be no stray whiskers to cause a short circuit when the conductors are inserted in their terminals.
Circular braided Measure the length of braiding to be removed and cut it off with a sharp knife. Trim off the frayed edges and any textile fillers inside the braid and slip a rubber sleeve over the end to prevent further fraying. Strip the required length of insulation from each core and twist the wires together as before.
Twisted twin Since this type has no sheathing, you only need to strip insulation and twist the cores together.

Stripping cable
The method for stripping cable is basically the same as for stripping flex, but you must take extra care not to damage the conductors since cable is expensive to replace.
Sheathed Measure and strip off the required amount of sheathing using a knife and pliers as previously described. Strip off the insulation from each wire and slip a length of green (or green/ yellow) PVC sleeving over the end of the earth wire. With the smallest cables (1.0 and 1.5sq mm), double the bared ends to provide greater contact area in the terminals. Cables of 4sq mm and above have stranded conductors and the ends must be twisted together with pliers.
Non-sheathed single core An example of this is the green/yellow PVC insulated earth cable; simply remove the insulation with wire strippers as described above.

Joining flex

One of the real dangers involving electricity is the joining up of flex, which can be a fire hazard. If you really have to do this job, always use a proper connector and check you have wired it up in the correct way.

Whenever possible avoid joining flex. If you have to, always use a proper connector and never try to join two pieces of flex by twisting the bare wires together and covering them with insulating tape. No matter how careful you are there is always a danger the join may work loose or come apart because it is suddenly stretched. If a join does work loose it can create sparks that may in turn lead to a fire. Among the other hazards, the earth safety lead may become detached in a three core flex join or the essential separation between the live and neutral wires break down, causing a short circuit.

Flex connectors are useful for portable appliances like irons and hairdryers, if you want to use them some distance from a socket. But never use more than one connector on a length of flex and don't trail it under carpets, up the stairs or across a passageway. Apart from the electrical dangers, there is always the risk someone might trip over it. When you require temporary lighting for a Christmas tree, for example, the flex and connector should be tucked against a skirting board and secured with adhesive tape, never by staples.

Before you decide you need to make a connection, consider whether it is easier, possibly cheaper, and certainly safer to buy a longer length of flex and fit it permanently to the lamp or appliance. Alternatively it could be preferable, though more expensive, to have a new power socket fitted, especially if it is for a semi-permanent appliance like a fridge, television or room heater.

Fitting connectors
Proper flex connectors do not only keep the cores separate but the screw terminals keep them securely fixed. Always use the same kind of flexes when making a join; although they need not be the same exterior colour, the amps and number of cores must match – three core must be matched with three core and two core with two core.

Only trim sufficient outer insulating sheath and inner insulation to leave the minimum bare wire to enter the connector terminals. Make sure there are no bare strands of wire exposed by twisting together the strands in each core before connecting. Always connect the brown core with brown, the blue with blue and the green/yellow earth with earth and check the plug at the end of the extension flex is correctly wired and fused.

Types of connectors
Three kinds of connectors are available for use in the home. But check which one is most suitable for the type of appliance involved and where it is to be used.

Connector strips Sometimes called block connectors, they are made of plastic and pairs of screws hold the flex ends. The plastic section can be cut to suit single, two or three core flex, but since the

screw heads are not insulated they are only suitable where they can be protected and insulated, such as inside a table lamp or appliance, or in a plastic box with a screw-down cover.

Insulated flex connectors These consist of a screw-down plastic cover with screw terminals inside. You buy them to suit the flex and the appliance: 5amp for small lamps and 13amp for most other uses. They are generally designed to accommodate the live, neutral and earth of three core flex but can be used with two core flex.

Insulated detachable flex connectors Made of rubber or a tough plastic, these are like a self-contained plug and socket and strong enough for outdoor use. They are available in 5 and 13amp sizes. You must always fix the 'male' or plug part of the connector on the flex leading to the appliance and the 'female' or socket half should be connected with the flex end that will be joined to the plug connecting with the mains. If you join them the other way round and they become detached, the part with the pins would be live to the touch – and therefore very dangerous.

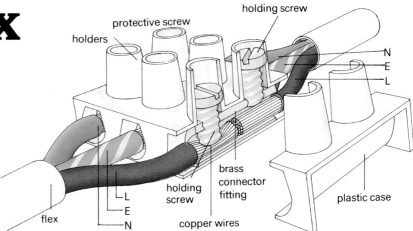

Connector strip

Above Plastic connector strip can be cut to suit single, two or three core flex
Below Insulated flex connector suitable for extending portable appliances such as hair dryers
Bottom Insulated detachable flex connector. Plug half must be connected to flex from appliance

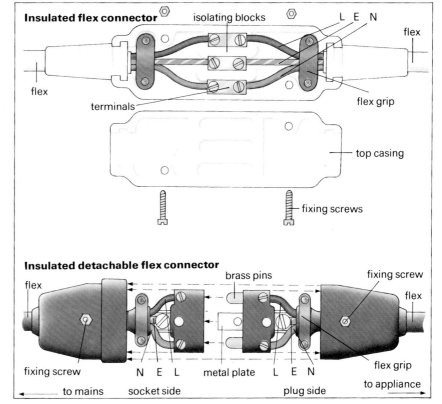

Wiring plugs

Probably the most common electrical job in the home is wiring a plug. It is crucial that the right core is fitted to the right terminal and that all connections are tight.

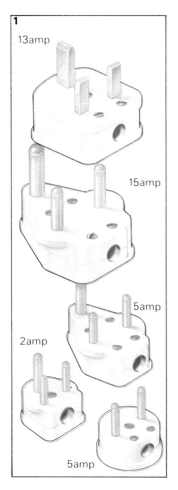

1 Types of plug: 13amp square pin; 15, 5 and 2amp round pin
2 Always check flex colour coding as right core must go to right plug terminal

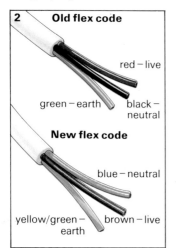

Houses that have been wired or rewired in Britain since 1947 will be fitted with ring main circuits. These are continuous loops of cable linking all wall sockets. The sockets are uniform 13amp outlets with rectangular holes to take the three flat pins of 13amp plugs.

This type of plug is supplied with a 3 or 13amp cartridge fuse (colour coded red and brown respectively). Always fit the fuse recommended by the manufacturer; as a general guide 3amp fuses are used with appliances rated up to 720 watts (for example table lamps) and 13amp fuses are used with larger appliances rated above 720 watts and up to 3000 watts (including kettles, irons and heaters). Some appliances (such as colour televisions, vacuum cleaners and spin dryers) although rated at less than 720 watts require a high starting current and should be used with 13amp fuses. In every case check first with maker's instructions.

Older houses will have radial wiring where separate cables radiate from the fuse board to each socket. These sockets are usually round pin in three sizes. The largest takes a 15amp plug used with larger appliances (such as heaters) while the other sizes take 5 and 2amp plugs used with smaller appliances (drills and table lamps respectively). The outlets may have two or three holes. The two pin sockets are not earthed and should only be used for light fixings with no exposed metal parts or for small double insulated appliances designed to operate without an earth connection and which are supplied only with two core flex.

Where possible it is safer to have radial wiring replaced (by your Electricity Board or a registered electrical contractor) with the properly earthed – and safer – ring main circuit.

Most plugs are made of tough, hard plastic but special rubberized types are available for equipment likely to be subjected to rough treatment, such as electric drills. Always buy a reputable make of plug because on poorer quality types the pins may move and cause a bad connection.

To fit a plug

First familiarize yourself with the colour code of the flex as it is most important the right core goes with the right terminal. With the new code blue is neutral, brown live and yellow/green earth. On older flex black is neutral, red live and green earth.

Remove the cover of the plug by undoing the large screw between the pins. When you look at the plug, with the largest pin (the earth) at the top and the flex outlet at the bottom, the live terminal is on the right (marked L) and the neutral terminal is on the left (marked N).

Prepare the flex by removing about 38mm (1½in) of the outer covering with a knife and fit the flex through the flex grip. This will be either a clamp type secured with two small screws (in which case loosen the screws, thread the flex through the grip and tighten the screws) or a V-shaped grip which

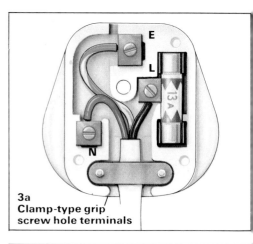

3a Clamp-type grip screw hole terminals

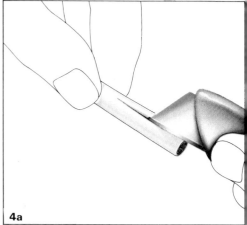

4a

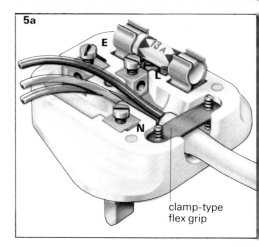

5a

clamp-type flex grip

Earthing

When rewiring a plug make absolutely sure the earth wire (yellow/green or green) is properly connected. If it is not you run the risk of an electric shock should the metal casing of an appliance become accidentally live.

The only appliances which do not need earthing are double insulated ones supplied with two core flex and mains operated shavers which are intended for use with special shaver sockets.

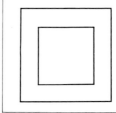

Left symbol for double insulation

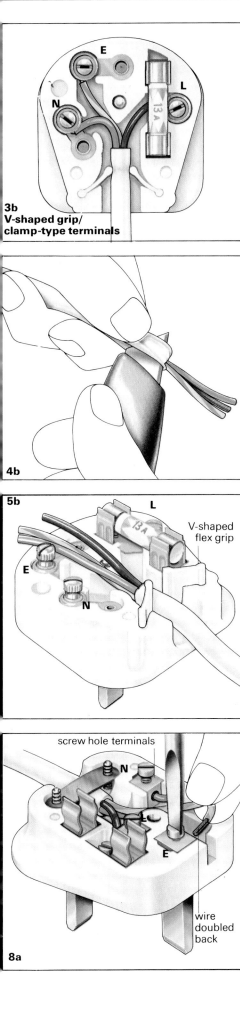

3b
**V-shaped grip/
clamp-type terminals**

4b

holds about 6mm (¼in) of the flex covering inside the plug. Make sure each core of the flex will reach its terminal, then cut 12mm (½in) beyond this for joining to the terminals. With wire strippers carefully remove about 12mm (½in) of the insulation at the end of each core and twist the loose strands neatly together.

Check which type of terminals the plug has. If it has screw holes double back the wires, insert them into the terminal holes and tighten the terminal screws with a small screwdriver to secure the wires. If the terminals are of the clamp type remove the screws, wrap the wires around the terminal posts in a clockwise direction, replace the screws and tighten them. On some plugs the live terminal is under the fuse housing, in which case you will have to remove the fuse before wiring that terminal. Make sure the plug is neatly wired: the insulation must go right up to the terminals and there must not be any straggling wires.

If a fuse is required simply snap the cartridge into the holding clips. Finally double check wires are connected to correct terminals before refitting cover. **Warning** If a plug gets hot the terminal screws may have worked loose and need to be tightened. Always replace a cracked plug immediately; never repair it, even temporarily, with insulating tape since there is a considerable risk the casing will come apart as the plug is put into or removed from the socket and you could get an electric shock.

It is important to check the flex regularly since the point where it joins the plug is particularly susceptible to breaking and fraying (especially on irons and vacuum cleaners). At first sign of wear cut frayed piece to make new end and rewire plug.

3a Screw hole terminals and clamp-type flex grip
3b Clamp-type terminals and V-shaped flex grip
4a Remove outer insulation by cutting along its length with sharp knife
4b Bend insulation away from flex and cut through fold
5a To insert flex in clamp-style grip, undo retaining screws, thread flex through grip and tighten screws
5b With V-shaped grip, simply push flex between two plastic strips
6 Check flex cores will reach terminals, allow 12mm (½in) extra for joining and cut off excess. Carefully remove insulation with wire strippers or sharp knife
7 Twist strands of each core neatly together

5b

L

V-shaped
flex grip

E

N

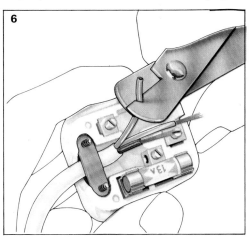

6

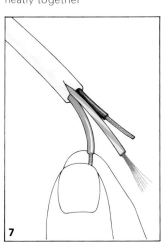

7

8a With screw hole terminals, double back wires, loosen terminal screws and insert wires in terminals. Gently tighten screws, taking care not to sever wires
8b With clamp terminals, remove screws and wrap bare wires round terminal posts in clockwise direction. Replace screws and tighten

screw hole terminals

N

E

wire doubled back

8a

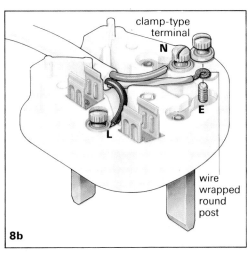

clamp-type terminal

N

E

L

wire wrapped round post

8b

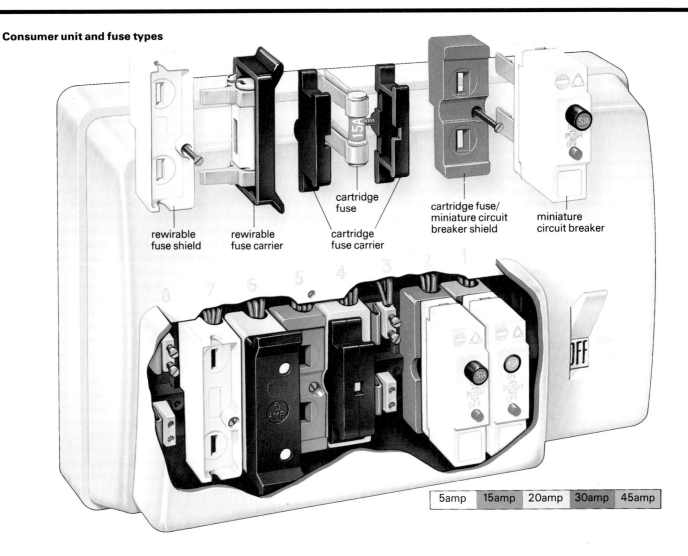

rewirable
fuse shield

rewirable
fuse carrier

cartridge
fuse

cartridge
fuse carrier

cartridge fuse/
miniature circuit
breaker shield

miniature
circuit breaker

| 5amp | 15amp | 20amp | 30amp | 45amp |

Repairing fuses

When electric current passes through a wire it causes heating: the thinner the wire the greater the heat. Even the thick wire used in domestic wiring will overheat if too much current passes through it – and may easily set the house on fire. To prevent this, a fuse is built into every circuit. This is a particularly thin piece of wire which will heat up quickly and melt if a more than safe quantity of current passes through it.

Types of fuses
All master fuses – one for each circuit – are mounted on fuse carriers in a fuse box close to the Electricity Board's supply meter. There are two main types, rewirable and cartridge, although miniature circuit breakers are widely used now on new installations.
Rewirable This type has fuse wire stretched between two retaining screws on the porcelain or plastic fuse carrier. The wire is available in three ratings – 5, 15 and 30amp – and you can usually buy a card of wire carrying a supply of all three.
Cartridge This type cannot be rewired since the fuse is sealed inside a tube; once it blows the fuse must be replaced. The advantage of the master cartridge fuse is it is impossible to fit the wrong one

because with the exception of 15- and 20-amp fuses, each of the other cartridges is a different size. The fuses are also colour coded so they can be easily recognized: 5amp is white, 15amp blue, 20amp yellow, 30amp red and 45amp green.
Miniature circuit breakers Used in domestic fuse boxes instead of fuses, these automatically switch themselves off if a circuit is overloaded. When the fault has been corrected the circuit can be reconnected just by resetting the on/off switch.

Why fuses blow
A master fuse will blow if the circuit is overloaded, if the fuse wire is of too low a rating or if a faulty appliance is used with an unfused plug or socket. Before repairing the fuse check you are not using too many appliances on one circuit and make sure you are using the right size fuse for the circuit. If you suspect a faulty appliance, even though it seems to be working adequately, stop using it and call an electrician or contact the manufacturer.

Sometimes a fuse blows simply because it is old; all you need to do is replace it with a new one of the correct rating. If a fuse still blows after being replaced, call an electrician.

Labelled fuse box cover

Above Repairing rewirable fuse. **Left** Turn off mains supply and remove blown fuse.
Centre Loosen retaining screws, remove old wire and thread in new wire. **Right** Wind wires round screws in clockwise direction and tighten screws
Below Use metal-cased torch to check if cartridge fuse has blown. Remove base of torch; place one end of fuse on torch casing and other end on bottom of battery. If bulb does not light when torch is on, fuse has blown

Below right Never replace a correct fuse with a larger one, which will carry more current than is safe before blowing.
For lighting circuit (up to 1kW) – 5amp
For immersion heater (3–4.8kW) – 15/20amp
For ring main circuit (up to 7.2kW) – 30amp
For cooker (up to 10.8kW) – 45amp

Warning Don't try to stop a fuse blowing by putting in a higher rated one.

Tracing faults

If one of your lights goes out see first whether those nearby are still working; if they are it is likely only the lamp bulb has blown. If all your lights are out check whether the street or your neighbours are in darkness too; if they are there is nothing wrong with your fuses – there is a general power failure and you will just have to wait for the power to be restored. If everyone else's lights are working you have an internal power failure, so turn off the relevant switch before investigating.

You will save time and trouble by keeping a small electrical screwdriver, a torch and replacement fuses or fuse wire handy by the fuse box. A supply of candles in the house is also good sense.

Rewiring fuses

Always turn off the mains supply switch before attempting any repairs. If you are really efficient you will have made a numbered plan of the carriers in your fuse box, labelling each one according to the circuit it controls (cooker, downstairs sockets,

upstairs lights etc.). This plan should be taped on the inside of the fuse box door so, when investigating a blown fuse, you can pick out the relevant carrier first time.

If you have not labelled them you must pull out each carrier in turn to find the blown fuse – look for one which has a broken or melted fuse wire. Undo the screws which clamp the fuse wire in place and remove the remains of the old wire. Stretch a new wire of the correct rating loosely between the screws and wind the ends in a clockwise direction round the screws, which must be carefully tightened until the wire is firmly held. Replace the fuse holder and close the fuse box before reconnecting the supply.

Replacing cartridge fuses

The only way of telling which cartridge fuse has blown is to remove one carrier at a time. Turn off the mains switch, remove a carrier, close the fuse box cover and switch on the mains supply. If everything else continues to work you have found the failed fuse. Take out the cartridge and replace it with a new one of the correct rating, refit the fuse carrier, close the box cover and turn on the main switch.

Cartridge fuses

5A

15A

20A

30A

45A

Moving and adding sockets

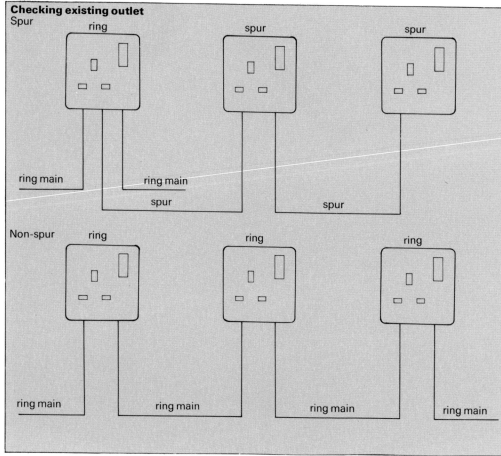

Checking existing outlet

Spur — ring — spur — spur

ring main — ring main — spur — spur

Non-spur — ring — ring — ring

ring main — ring main — ring main — ring main

Before you start work check to make sure the outlet you want to run your spur from is not itself already a spur. Sockets with only one cable are definitely spur sockets, and cannot be used. Sockets with two cables may be on the ring (left, bottom), but may also be on an old two-socket spur (left, top); these are now no longer permitted by the Wiring Regulations. You can test which is which with a continuity tester. Turn off the power at the mains and disconnect the circuit cables; then link the live cores with the test probes. If the socket is on the ring the test light will come on; if it is on a spur, it will not

Electricity is one energy source you can switch on where and when you want it. There is no reason to run a power tool off an extension from the kitchen when you need to work in the garage – or to unplug the bedside lamp when you want to use a portable television in the bedroom. The answer is to provide more socket outlets, a job you can do yourself safely if you follow the correct procedure.

Unless you were lucky enough to have supervised the installation of power points when your house was being built, you may find you have too few sockets and some that are in the wrong place. Moving sockets, adding extra ones or converting a single to a double (or twin) socket are jobs well within the capabilities of the amateur if you follow instructions carefully and make it a golden rule to switch off at the mains whenever you tackle any electrical work. A great part of the work is non-electrical: lifting floorboards to trace cables, drilling holes between joists for new cables or cutting back plastered walls and replastering them after you have buried the new cable and connected the new outlets.

Most homes take their power supply from ring circuits – but it is possible that your home's 13amp socket outlets may be on a radial circuit. This circuit consists of a number of outlets and fixed appliances supplied by one cable, from the consumer unit, which ends at the last outlet. This is quite different from the old radial system of 15amp plugs (with round pins) in which numerous 15amp circuits radiated from a multi-way fuseboard.

These old installations are being phased out; if you still have this system, it could be in a dangerous condition and you should ask your Electricity Board to check the wiring – something the Electricity Council recommends people should have done every five years.

Connecting methods

There are three ways of connecting extra sockets or fixed appliances to the domestic ring circuit, all of which can be handled by the consumer.

Loops By taking a direct loop from the terminals of an existing socket outlet.

Junction box By inserting a junction box in the ring cable – generally under the floor – and taking one or two sockets from that.

Consumer unit By running a separate cable from the consumer unit.

Sockets connected by way of loops or junction boxes are called spurs; you can take only one new socket on a spur from any existing socket or from a newly installed junction box. Spurs not only supply extra socket outlets but can also be used to supply a fixed appliance, such as a wall heater.

Flush-fitted box

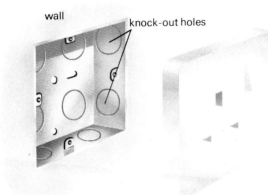

wall · knock-out holes

Surface mounted box

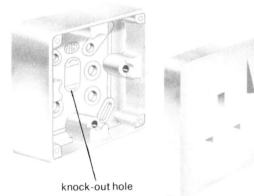

knock-out hole

Here a fused switch connection – placed close to the appliance – replaces a socket outlet. Some fixed connections incorporate a pilot light to show when the appliance is on. Each spur may feed one single socket outlet, one double socket outlet or one fixed appliance.

Generally there is one ring circuit for each floor in a house. You should run your loop or junction box from the nearest existing socket outlet or nearest accessible part of the ring circuit to the new outlet. If you want to run the spur from a socket, make sure the outlet is not itself a spur. Undo the screws on the front plate and gently pull the outlet from the wall box and examine the wiring. If there are two red, two black and two earth (possibly green-sleeved or bare) conductors in the box, the outlet is probably not a spur. To make quite sure examine the nearest socket outlets each side of it. If there is only one set of conductors on these, your original choice is already a spur and should not be used. If neither outlet is a spur, then you know you can loop out of the first one you examined. Replace the frontplates and switch the mains back on until you are ready to begin work.

Planning outlets

While you are planning for extra outlets, you must decide what type of fitting you want. The choice is between flush-fitted sockets or sockets on wall-mounted boxes. More work is involved in installing the flush type, but the wall-mounted

socket can be an obstruction to furniture and vacuum cleaners at ground level and can rob you of space when fitted above a work surface.

If you are in the habit of using an adaptor plug on some of your existing outlets, it may be worth investing in a double (or twin) socket and changing that for the single while you are working on the terminals behind it.

Socket height Socket outlets should not be less than 150mm (6in) above the floor or above a working surface in the kitchen or elsewhere. In rooms being used by elderly people or active invalids, outlets should be 1m (or 3ft) from the floor to eliminate bending.

Cable The cable used in a ring circuit is 2.5sq mm and the usual type for domestic installations is polyvinyl chloride (pvc) sheathed twin and earth, or may be tough rubber sheathed (trs) cable. Older ring circuits are wired in the Imperial-sized cable (called 7/029), which has seven strands. But it is quite all right to use the metric-size cable when adding to a ring circuit wired with 7/029 cable.

Decide carefully where your new cable will run. There will be problems, for example, if you have a modern house or flat in which underfloor wiring on the ground floor was installed before a solid floor was laid. The costly solution to this, in terms of cable, may be that you will have to run cable from the consumer unit up to the first floor, under the floorboards and then trail it down the cavity of the wall to the position of your intended outlet. Alternatively you could bury the cable in the plasterwork (the cable does not need any additional insulation) or run it on the surface of the wall – in which case you must clad it in a plastic conduit. Surface cables look unsightly in living rooms and create a further problem when decorating.

Another method is to remove your existing skirting and replace it with ducting, in metal or plastic, designed to house cables. Never consider cutting sockets into existing skirting boards. It is dangerous, illegal and may invalidate any insurance claim in the event of a fire.

If you do have a solid floor and need only one or two extra socket outlets, you will find it simpler to loop out of an existing outlet and bury the new cable in the wall.

Cutting plaster

There are two methods of making a channel in plaster. You can do it with a club hammer and brick bolster after first scoring with a sharp knife two straight lines in the plaster along the intended cable route, chipping out the depth you require. Or you can use a specially designed router, which works off an electric drill at a slow speed. Before you start routing you must drill a series of guide holes along the intended cable route. It is unlikely your plaster will not be deep enough to take a cable, but if you are unlucky you will just have to get to work again with the chisel.

Before you start laying cable, prepare the recesses or mountings for new sockets or position the junction boxes – preferably out of sight beneath floorboards. Where you run cables across joists you should run them through holes drilled at least 50mm (2in) below the top of the joists. Never lay cable in the grooves cut in the tops of joists because of the danger from nails that may be driven through and penetrate the cables.

When replacing floorboards, use screws instead of nails, which will enable you to identify the cable

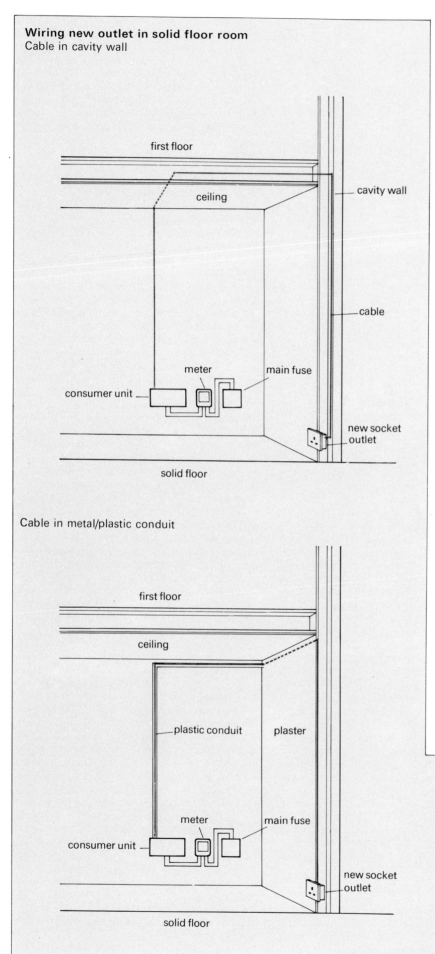

Wiring new outlet in solid floor room
Cable in cavity wall

first floor

ceiling

cavity wall

cable

meter

main fuse

consumer unit

new socket
outlet

solid floor

Cable in metal/plastic conduit

first floor

ceiling

plastic conduit   plaster

meter

main fuse

consumer unit

new socket
outlet

solid floor

run and to reach it more quickly on future occasions. Before replacing the boards you should cut out a small section of the board at the skirting board end to protect cable running up or down the wall, behind skirting and then under the boards.

Warning Care must be taken not to damage any existing cables or pipes. Make sure current is turned off at the main; gas and water should also be turned off.

Wall sockets

Cutting out the recess for a flush socket box is quite simple. Mark on the wall in pencil an outline of the knock-out box, score the lines with a sharp knife and, using a brick bolster and club hammer, chip away until you reach the brickwork. Drill a series of close-spaced holes all round and then chip away another layer until you reach the required depth. Test the knock-out box fits, knock out the required access holes in it (sharp taps with a cold chisel are usually enough) and fix a grommet in each hole. This is a rubber or plastic ring, with an exterior slot which fits neatly in the hole, to protect the cable. Drill the mounting holes, plug them and screw the knock-out box into the recess, making good the edges with plaster.

Fixing a wall-mounted box is much easier. You only need to channel out enough plaster to accommodate the cable run from the floorboards and behind the skirting (unless it is being channelled into a wall from another socket) and into the box, which is plugged and screwed to the wall.

Moving existing sockets

If you intend to line your rooms with plasterboard or panel boards fixed to battens, you must plan how you are going to reposition your existing outlets. If you already have wall-mounted sockets, you can cut a snug opening into your lining where each socket is situated, turning the outlets into flush fittings. If your existing outlets are flush fitting, with a knock-out box recessed into the original wall, you have several alternatives.

You can check, by easing the knock-out box from the wall, whether there is enough slack cable on the ring to allow you to move the entire outlet forward to the new surface. If there is plenty of slack, you can fit a new wall-mounted box and reconnect to the socket terminals. If there is not enough cable, check whether the cable is fed from above or below. In each instance you will probably be able to find enough cable to enable you to reposition the outlet either higher or lower than it was on the old wall. But remember, the socket

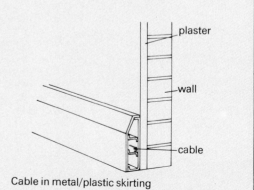

plaster

wall

cable

Cable in metal/plastic skirting

Marking box position

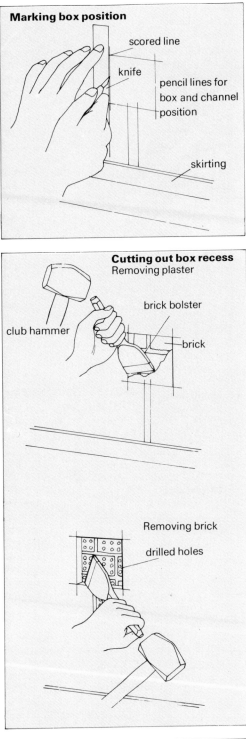

scored line

knife

pencil lines for box and channel position

skirting

Cutting out box recess
Removing plaster

club hammer

brick bolster

brick

Removing brick

drilled holes

Running cable under floorboards

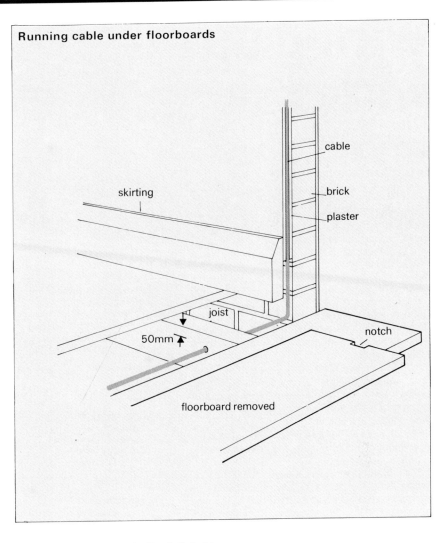

skirting

cable

brick

plaster

joist

50mm

notch

floorboard removed

Knocking out holes in flush-fitted box

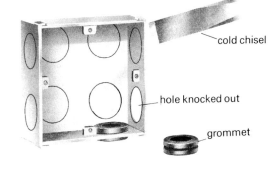

cold chisel

hole knocked out

grommet

Cutting out channel with router

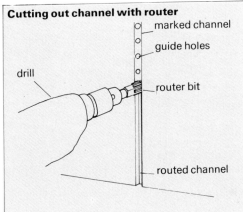

marked channel

guide holes

drill

router bit

routed channel

should be at least 150mm (6in) above the floor and never be installed in a skirting board.

If this is also impossible, you will have to fit a three-way terminal block into the existing knock-out box, which converts it into a junction box. You must run cable from a knock-out hole (not forgetting to use a grommet) at the top or bottom of the box and use this to feed one single or one double wall-mounted socket outlet positioned nearby on your new wall. You must also cover the modified knock-out box with a blank plate.

Wiring up sockets

Electricity can be supplied where you want it, as long as you have enough outlets. You can install new power points or move existing ones yourself.

Having done all the non-electrical work such as lifting boards, chanelling plaster to take cables, or cutting recesses for the new knock-out boxes and installing them, it is time to start wiring with 2.5sq mm twin core and earth PVC sheathed cable. This is quite simple and safe if you turn off the mains before you start work.

Changes to the Regulations

The latest (15th) edition of the IEE Wiring Regulations contains a significant change as far as adding spurs to existing circuits is concerned. It was permitted to extend ring circuits by adding spurs feeding *two* single sockets, one double socket or one fixed appliance; now a spur may feed only *one* outlet of any type, whether it is a socket outlet or a fused connection unit.

The new Regulations allow spurs to be connected to modern radial circuits too, with the same restrictions applying.

Since many homes will already contain spurs feeding two sockets, it is therefore extremely important to check whether any socket to which a spur is being attached is actually on the main circuit.

A socket with two cables connected to it could be one on a ring circuit, an intermediate socket on a modern radial circuit or the first socket on an old two-socket spur. You can tell the first and third possibilities apart using a continuity tester (see page 248). To identify the second, check which circuit supplies it at the main consumer unit; radial power circuits have only one circuit cable connected to the circuit fuseway, while ring circuits have two.

Loops

If you are running a loop from the back of an existing socket to connect to a new spur socket outlet or a fixed appliance, you must start by cutting your cable to length. Since you will need to feed about 125mm (5in) of cable into the recessed knock-out box, surface-mounted box or junction box from which the new spur will receive its power, remove about 100mm (4in) from the outer sheath and then strip about 15mm ($\frac{5}{8}$in) of the insulation material from the red and black conductors. The earth conductor will be bare and you should slip on a short length of green/yellow PVC sleeving (generally available where you buy twin core and earth cable), leaving just 15mm ($\frac{5}{8}$in) bare at the end.

You are now ready to run the cable into its channelling or under the floor, depending on the route you have chosen. Cable under floors should be run in holes drilled at least 50mm (2in) below the top of joists and secured only by cable fixing clips. If you are running cable in plaster, you should wedge it in position while you are connecting up. The cable sometimes wriggles free and if this

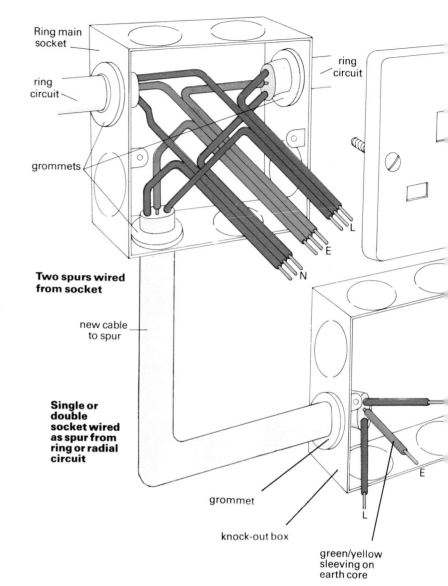

Ring main socket

ring circuit

grommets

Two spurs wired from socket

ring circuit

L
E
N

new cable to spur

Single or double socket wired as spur from ring or radial circuit

grommet

knock-out box

L
E

green/yellow sleeving on earth core

happens you should secure it with a couple of dabs of contact adhesive – but make sure the cable is in the right place.

Socket to socket

Thread the 125mm (5in) of unsheathed conductors into the knock-out hole you have prepared (into which you must always place a rubber or plastic grommet as protection for the cable) and loosen the wires on the terminals on the back of the socket plate. Arrange the new conductors alongside the entwined pairs already there; red with reds, black with blacks and earth (or green) with earths. Put each set of three wires in their respective terminals. Reds go to the live terminal, blacks to the neutral terminal and greens to the earth terminal. All terminals are clearly marked on the back of the socket plate. Tighten the terminal screws, check the conductors are secure and replace the front of the socket outlet.

You can now connect the spur to the new outlet. Simply enter the spur knock-out box in the way described and connect each of the three conductors

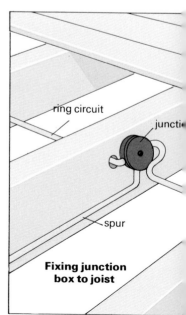

ring circuit

junctio

spur

Fixing junction box to joist

Socket wired to fused connection unit

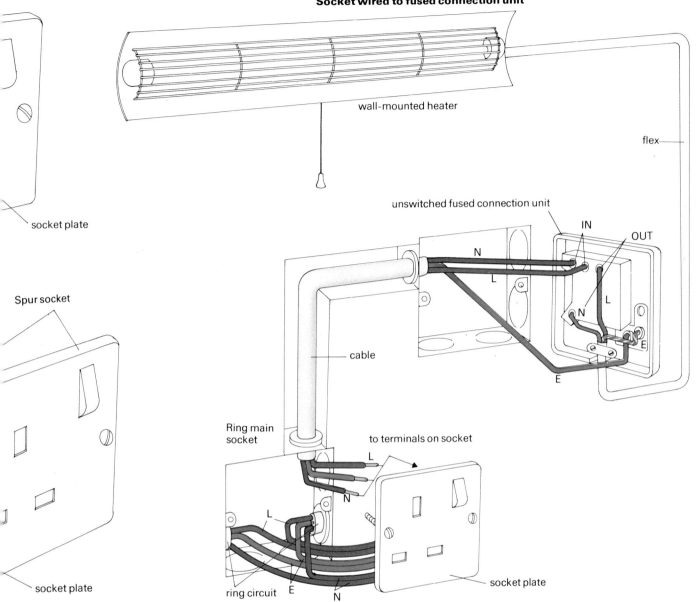

wall-mounted heater

flex

socket plate

Spur socket

unswitched fused connection unit

IN

OUT

N

L

L

N

E

cable

E

Ring main socket

to terminals on socket

L

N

L

ring circuit   E   N

socket plate

socket plate

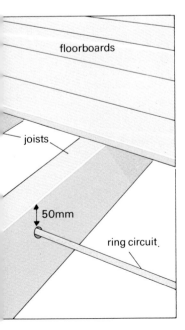

floorboards

joists

50mm

ring circuit

to its relevant terminal. Screw the socket plate on, plug in an appliance that you know is working, turn on the mains and switch on at the new outlet. If the appliance works, your wiring is correct. Only then – and again with the mains switched off – should you plaster the cable into the wall or replace the floorboards.

Sockets on stud partition walls
Mounting socket outlets on plasterboard-covered stud partition walls used to involve either cutting away part of the stud to get a secure fixing or using fiddly retaining clips. It is now possible to buy a flush mounting box which has spring-loaded lugs at each side; this is simply pushed into place in the prepared cut-out, ready to receive the spur cable and socket outlet faceplate.

Fused connection unit
Follow the same wiring procedure if you are running a loop from a socket outlet (or a junction box) to a fused (switched or unswitched) connection unit for connecting with a fixed appliance, such as

a wall-mounted heater. At the connection unit there are six terminals – two live, two neutral and two earth. The live and neutral conductors from the loop cable must be connected to the terminals marked IN. The other terminals are marked OUT and to these you connect the live and neutral leads in the appliance's flex, feeding the flex in through a knock-out hole at the bottom of the unit. The earth leads can connect to either of the two earth terminals. When this is done, check the wiring.
Warning Check there is a 3 or 13amp cartridge fuse in the pull-out holder at the front of the unit (manufacturers sometimes forget to include one) and do not be too violent in clearing the knock-out hole or you may shatter the plastic casing. Never connect to an appliance rated at more than 13amp (or 3kW), because it will need a separate circuit from the consumer unit.

Junction boxes
If you are supplying your extra sockets or fused connection unit through a junction box, you will already have sited this within reach of the ring

circuit cable and secured it to a joist, a short length of timber between joists or another suitable timber fixture. Knock out three holes: for the ring cable to enter and leave the junction box and a third for the spur cable, which should be prepared as already explained. There are three terminals in the box: live, neutral and earth. It does not matter which you use as long as you are consistent – but it is bad practice not to connect to the properly designated terminals. Try to avoid cutting the ring cable. You should be able to strip away the outer sheath and cut away enough insulation at a suitable point so there is sufficient bare wire to lay in the terminal (with the corresponding conductors from the spur cable) under the terminal screws. Connect the other end of the new cable as already described, either to a new socket outlet or to a fixed connection unit.

Terminal block conversion

If you are turning an existing outlet into a junction box by using a three-way terminal block inside an existing recessed knock-out box or surface-mounted backplate, you must first remove a knock-out hole

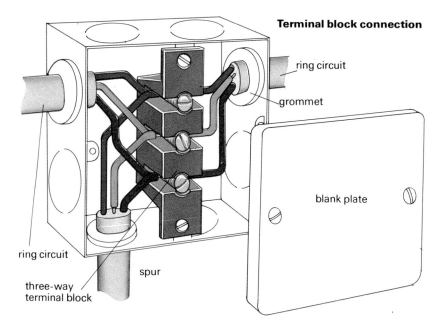

Terminal block connection

ring circuit

grommet

blank plate

ring circuit

spur

three-way terminal block

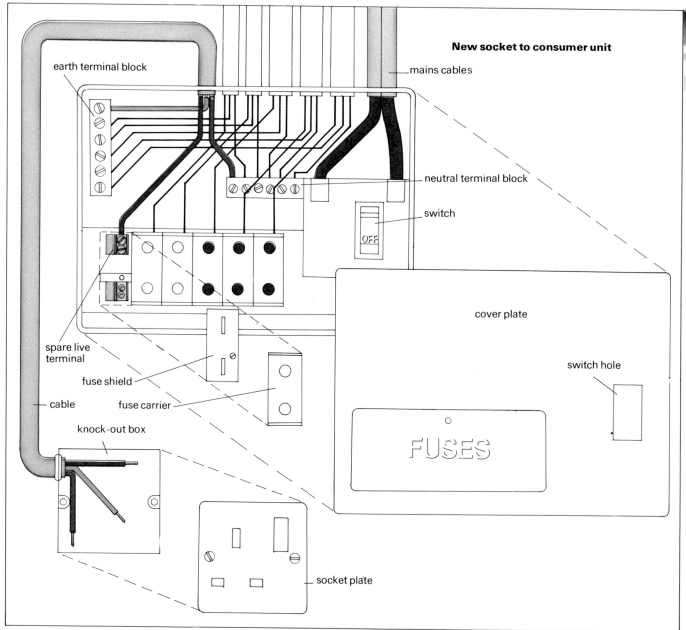

New socket to consumer unit

earth terminal block

mains cables

neutral terminal block

switch

OFF

cover plate

spare live terminal

switch hole

fuse shield

cable

fuse carrier

knock-out box

FUSES

socket plate

to get the new spur cable into the box. Connect the three sets of conductors and earths: the cable going into the existing socket and the cable leaving one single outlet, one double one or one fused connew spur cable, which can be used to connect either one or two spur outlets or one fused connection unit. Before connecting the spur, cover the knock-out box or backplate with a blank plate.

Consumer unit connection

If you are running an extra single socket outlet or a fused connection unit (up to 13amps) direct from the consumer unit, you wire the socket or unit in the normal way – but with only one set of conductors. The other end of the cable is fed directly into the consumer unit and great care must be taken here because a wrong connection could cause a lot of expensive damage.

The consumer unit is clearly marked inside: the red (live) wire from your cable must be connected to a spare live terminal block, the black conductor must be connected to a spare terminal on the neutral terminal block and the earth must be connected to its corresponding place on the earth terminal block. Use 2.5sq mm cable for the circuit, and fit a 20-amp fuse in the consumer unit.

Double socket

When you are replastering a single socket outlet or removing it to run off a spur, you should consider whether it is worthwhile replacing the outlet with a double (or twin) socket outlet. The terminal connections on double sockets match those on single outlets; all you have to do is exchange them.

The easiest method is to place a slim surface-mounted box over the recessed knock-out box (if you have one and provided you have enough cable). Smooth the edges of the entry hole with a file to ensure the stripped insulation does not chafe. You will probably have to secure the box to the wall with plugs each side of the old box, so take care not to drill into the ring circuit cable. If you have an existing surface-mounted box, you must remove this and replace both the backplate box and the socket outlet.

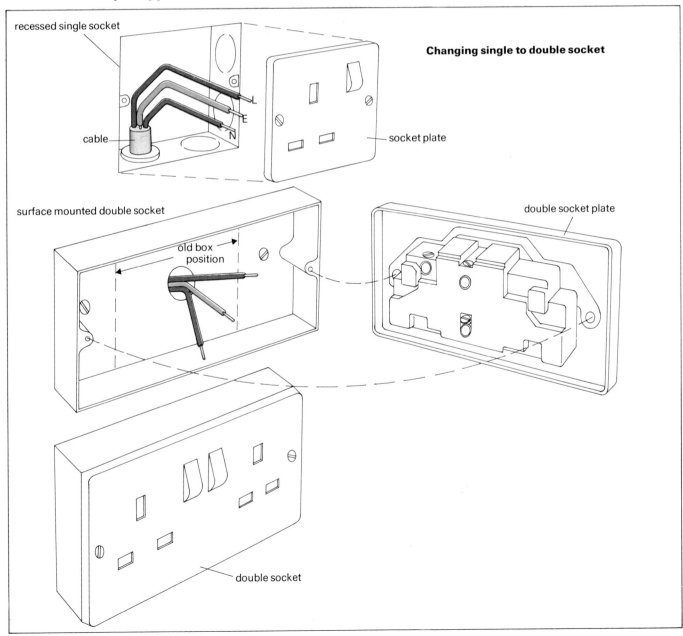

Changing single to double socket

recessed single socket

cable

socket plate

L
E
N

surface mounted double socket

old box position

double socket plate

double socket

Adding lights and switches

It is a simple operation to add an extra ceiling light, controlled by its own switch, to an existing lighting circuit. If as in most modern homes the wiring is flat twin PVC-sheathed cable, it is likely the loop-in system is used, which means an extension can be taken direct from an existing ceiling rose.

In recently wired installations the circuit cable also contains an earth continuity conductor (ecc), which is looped in and out of an earth terminal in the ceiling rose. If your lighting circuits are wired on the junction box system – common until the mid-1960s – there should normally be one junction box for every light and its switch.

Loop-in extension

Drill a 13mm ($\frac{1}{2}$in) diameter hole in the ceiling at the new light position and another hole in the ceiling immediately above the new switch position. Any floorboards above will have to be raised, as will some along the new cable route to gain access above the ceiling. Switch off at the mains and remove the ceiling rose and pendant flex at the connecting light. Take care not to separate joined wires; if necessary use insulation tape to keep them together temporarily.

Take your coil of 1sq mm two core and earth PVC-sheathed cable and mark 'mains' on the end of the sheath; push the end through the hole in the ceiling at the connecting light, leaving the existing wires protruding from the ceiling. Then pull through sufficient cable from the floor above (or in

the roof space) to reach the position above the new light. Thread the cable through holes drilled in the joists, at least 50mm (2in) below the top of the joists, and pass the end of the cable through the hole in the ceiling, leaving about 300mm (12in) for connections at the new rose. Cut the cable at the old ceiling rose position, leaving about the same amount for connections.

Take the cable coil to the switch position and push the end through the hole in the ceiling. From above, run it to the new light and pass the end down alongside the first cable marked 'mains'.

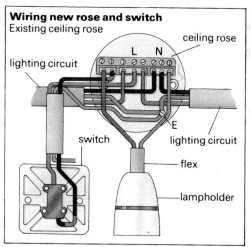

Wiring new rose and switch
Existing ceiling rose

ceiling rose

lighting circuit

switch

lighting circuit

flex

lampholder

E

L N

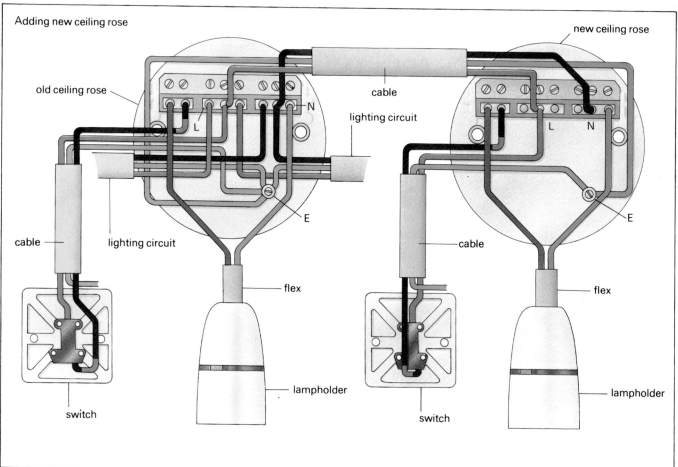

Adding new ceiling rose

new ceiling rose

old ceiling rose

cable

lighting circuit

N

L

E

cable

lighting circuit

flex

lampholder

switch

cable

L N

E

cable

flex

lampholder

switch

Mounting a new ceiling rose

If there is no suitable mounting for the new light, fix a piece of 100 × 25mm (4 × 1in) timber between the joists just above the ceiling, having first drilled a hole in the timber to take the two sheathed cables. Cut the cable at the switch position about 1.37m (4ft 6in) above floor level, leaving about 300mm (12in) for connections.

Knock out the thin plastic in the base of the ceiling rose, thread in the two cables and fix the rose to the ceiling with screws 25mm (1in) long. Strip about 50mm (2in) of sheathing from the end of the cable marked 'mains' and about 6mm ($\frac{1}{4}$in) of insulation from the end of the red and the black wire. Insert the bared end of the red conductor into one of the terminal holes in the live (centre) terminal and tighten the screw. Connect the black wire to the neutral terminal, using the middle hole. Push the cable slack back into the ceiling, making sure the end of the sheath will be within the rose.

Prepare the end of the other cable in the same way and connect the red wire into one of the other two holes in the live terminal. Slip a short piece of red PVC sleeving or insulation tape over the end of the black wire and insert this into the inner terminal hole of the two-hole (switch wire) terminal bank. Slip green/yellow PVC sleeving over the bare earth wires and connect them to the earth terminal.

Now connect the pendant flex. Strip about 75mm (3in) of sheath from the end of a length of two core flex. Bare the ends and connect the brown to the outer hole of the switch wire terminal and the blue to the outer hole of the neutral terminal. Tighten all terminal screws and hook the flex wires over the anchor pieces: thread on the rose cover and screw it to its base. Connect the lampholder to the other

end of the flex, using the same method as for the ceiling rose; if the unsheathed wires protrude from the cap, the flex wires must be shortened.

Connecting a switch

If the switch is to be surface-mounted, take the plastic surface box and knock out a thin section for the cable. Hold the box in position against the wall and mark the fixing holes. Drill and plug them to take No 8 screws. If the switch is to be flush-mounted you must use a metal knock-out box. The cable from the ceiling to the box can be fixed to the surface, using plastic cable clips spaced no more than 400mm (16in) apart or buried in the plaster.

The end of the cable is stripped and the conductors prepared as for a ceiling rose. The red wire, which is the live feed, is connected to the common terminal. The black wire, the switch wire, is enclosed in a short piece of red PVC sleeving or PVC insulation tape and connected to the L2 terminal. The earth should be enclosed in green/yellow PVC sleeving and connected to the earth terminal in the mounting box. The switch is secured to its box by two screws supplied.

Replacing the existing rose

Replace the existing wires as before; if you had an old type ceiling rose, replace with a modern one with in-line shrouded terminals. Strip and prepare the end of the new cable as for the first ceiling rose. Connect the red wire to the centre terminal (alongside another red wire if there is no spare terminal hole), the black wire to the neutral terminal and the earth wire in green/yellow PVC sleeving to the earth terminal. Any existing unsleeved earth wires in the rose should be sleeved before reconnecting.

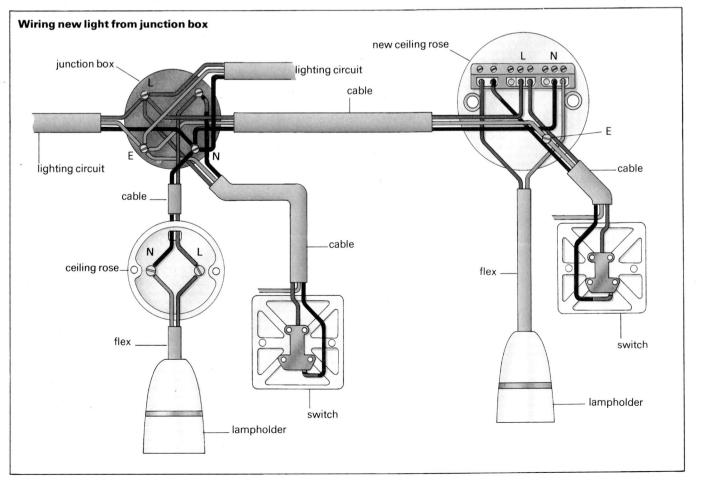

Wiring new light from junction box

junction box
lighting circuit
new ceiling rose
lighting circuit
cable
L   N
E
lighting circuit
cable
cable
ceiling rose
N   L
cable
cable
flex
flex
switch
switch
lampholder
lampholder

Junction box extension

After switching off the power, locate an existing, suitably placed junction box by lifting boards or checking in the roof space, unscrew the cover and examine the wires and terminals. The red live wire of the new cable is connected to the terminal having two or more red wires, the black neutral wire is connected to the terminal containing two or more black wires and the earth wire with its green/yellow sleeving goes to the terminal containing the earth wires. The remainder of the work is the same as when looping out of a ceiling rose to another rose.

Moving a light

When a ceiling light is to be moved, take down the existing pendant (having, of course, switched off the power) and pull back the cables into the ceiling space – taking care not to separate wires connected to any one terminal. Mark which of the two wires or sets of jointed wires were connected to the flex terminals, for it is from these the extension is made. Nail a piece of 100 × 25mm (4 × 1in) timber between the joists, about halfway down, and fix a four-terminal 5amp junction box to it. Drill a hole in the ceiling at the new position and lift boards and drill holes in the joists as necessary for the route of the new cable from the junction box to the light. Run a length of cable from the junction box to the light and pass the end through the hole in the ceiling. Connect the live wire to the switched live rose terminal, and the neutral and earth wires as before.

At the junction box, connect the existing wires to the box terminals. If the existing light was a loop-in ceiling rose, all four terminals in the box will be used. Otherwise only two, plus earth, will be needed. Prepare the end of the cable as already described and connect the red to the single wire which was connected to flex. If this is a black wire, enclose the end in red sleeving or PVC-insulated tape before connecting it to the junction box terminal. Connect the black wire to the terminal now containing one, two or more black wires and connect the earth with its green/yellow sleeving to the one containing the earth wires. If the circuit has no earth, connect it to a spare terminal. Replace the box cover.

Fitting an extra light

When you need an extra light that is to be controlled by an existing switch, follow the instructions given for moving a light, except that instead of using a junction box you leave the original light in position, install a new ceiling rose and connect the new cable to the existing ceiling rose terminals carrying the flex wires.

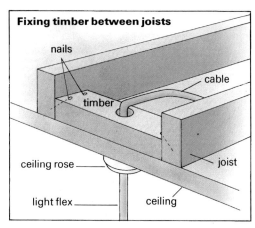

Fixing timber between joists

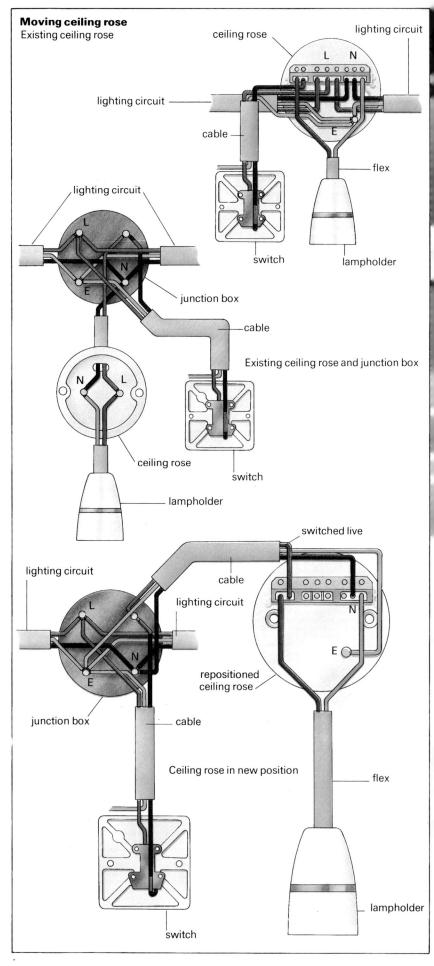

Moving ceiling rose
Existing ceiling rose

Existing ceiling rose and junction box

Ceiling rose in new position

Adding light using same switch
From loop-in rose

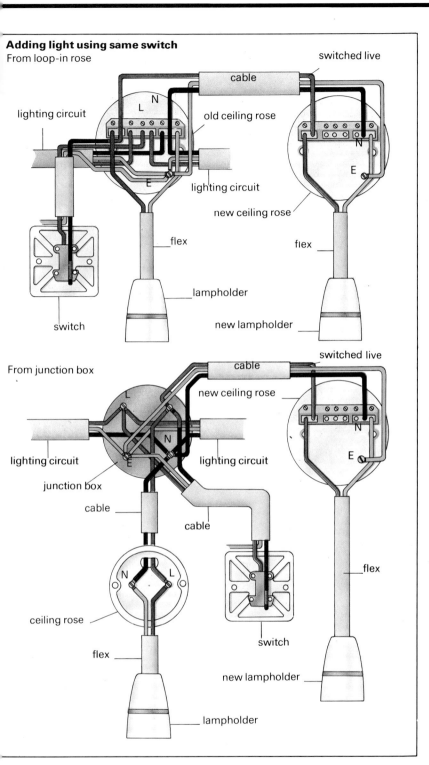

switched live

cable

lighting circuit

N
L

old ceiling rose

E

lighting circuit

new ceiling rose

flex

flex

lampholder

new lampholder

switch

From junction box

cable

switched live

new ceiling rose

L

lighting circuit

N

lighting circuit

E

junction box

cable

cable

N   L

flex

ceiling rose

switch

flex

new lampholder

lampholder

Fitting an extra switch

Adding a second switch to a lighting point, such as at the end of a hall or at the back door to provide another switch in a kitchen, not only adds to your convenience but probably helps you to save electricity. Replace the existing one-way switch with a two-way switch, install a two-way switch in the second position and link the two switches together by fitting a 1sq mm three core and earth PVC-sheathed cable.

If the existing switch is the modern square plate mounted on either a plastic surface box or a metal flush-mounted box, remove the existing switch, push the end of the new cable into the box through the existing grommet, run the cable up the wall through the ceiling, under the floorboards (or roof space) and down through the ceiling to the second switch position, where you fit either a surface or flush-mounted recess box.

Three terminals A two-way switch has three terminals – Common, L1 and L2. The two existing wires disconnected from the one-way switch are connected to terminals L1 and L2, although it does not matter which goes to which terminal. The three core and earth sheathed cable has three insulated wires: red, yellow and blue. The red wire goes to the Common terminal, the yellow wire to terminal L1 and the blue to L2. The earth in its green/yellow sleeving is connected to the earth terminal of the box. At the second switch there are only three new wires plus the earth. The red wire is connected to the Common terminal, the yellow to L1 and the blue to L2 and the green/yellow-sleeved earth to the box's earth terminal. Arrange the wires neatly in each box and secure the switches with the screws provided with the fitting.

Fitting a cord switch

Cord-operated ceiling switches are made in one and two-way versions; so in a bedroom, for example, you can fit a switch on the ceiling above the bed-head as well as the normal switch by the door. The three core cable is passed down through a hole in the ceiling instead of down the wall and the switch fixed to the ceiling. If necessary mount the switch on a piece of timber fixed between the joists, as already described. The connections are the same as for a wall switch.

Wiring extra switch

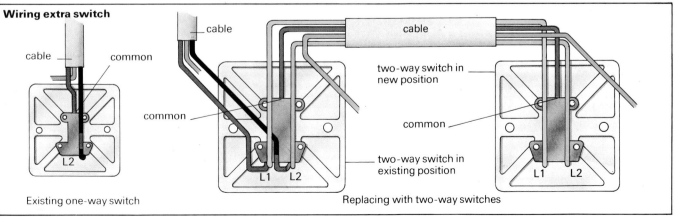

cable

cable

common

common

cable

two-way switch in new position

common

two-way switch in existing position

L2

L1   L2

L1   L2

Existing one-way switch

Replacing with two-way switches

Dimmers and time switches

The dimmer is an electronic device which contains a semi-conductor, associated components and a TV suppressor. But unlike the old resistor dimmer, which consumed unwanted wattage and became very hot, the modern version does not use a significant amount of electricity and can be regarded as an energy saver.

These switches have been designed to replace any one-way lighting switch of the square-plate pattern, simply by removing the existing switch and fitting the dimmer in its place; this is connected to the same wiring and does not require any modification to the circuit.

If you are replacing the old round (tumbler) switch mounted on a wood block or plastic plate (pattress), it is necessary to replace the block or pattress with a standard flush-mounting box.

Warning In all cases follow the manufacturer's instructions for fitting and always turn off the electricity at the mains before you start work.

Types of dimmer

The low-priced dimmer consists of a rotary action knob which reduces lighting from full brilliance down to off. This is adequate for most purposes, its one disadvantage being that the control has to be set each time the dimmer is switched on, since it has to be rotated through the full dimming operation to switch off the light.

There are many situations where it is more convenient to switch a dimmed light off and on without having to adjust the control; this can be achieved by fitting a combined dimmer and on-off switch. One type has a slide control for dimming; another has a milled-edge dial and a third a single push-on/pull-off control for switching.

Two-way switch A dimmer can be inserted in a two-way switching circuit to allow, for example, a landing light operated from both landing and hall to be dimmed as required. The dimmer switch can be fixed in any position, but for ease of wiring it is best installed near one of the two-way switches and preferably mounted on the same box, which would replace the existing one gang box (which takes a single switch).

To do this, remove the two-way switch and its box and fit a dual box, which in the case of a flush-mounted fitting will mean enlarging the recess in the plaster. A dual box is slightly larger than the ordinary two gang box (which takes two switches) used for double socket outlets and has two fixing lugs in the centre to take a fixing screw for each switch.

If the existing switch, in which a dimmer is to be incorporated, is a two gang unit controlling the hall and landing light, the two gang unit is retained. The dimmer, which is a one gang unit, must only be wired to control one of the lights.

Dimming two lights Dimmer switches with a single knob incorporating push-on/pull-off action are made in two gang versions to control two different lights.

Dimming part lighting A special combined dimmer,

1 Wiring for dimmer switch and for ordinary switch
2 Wiring two-way dimmer with ordinary two-way switch
3 Portable plug-in dimmer incorporating on/off switch
4 One or two-way dimmer with separate on/off switch
5 One or two-way dimmer with separate on/off switch
6 One or two-way combined dimmer and on/off switch
7 Light sensitive dimmer (on at dusk, off at dawn)
8 One or two-way combined dimmer and on/off switch with chrome finish
9 Master/slave touch dimmer
10 One or two-way sliding dimmer and separate on/off switch
11 Milled-edge drum dimmer and separate on/off switch
12 Combined dimmer and on/off switch which has facility to provide both dimmed and fixed lighting
13 One or two-way combined dimmer and on/off switch
14 Combined dimmer and on/off switch with chrome finish
15 Time lag dimmer

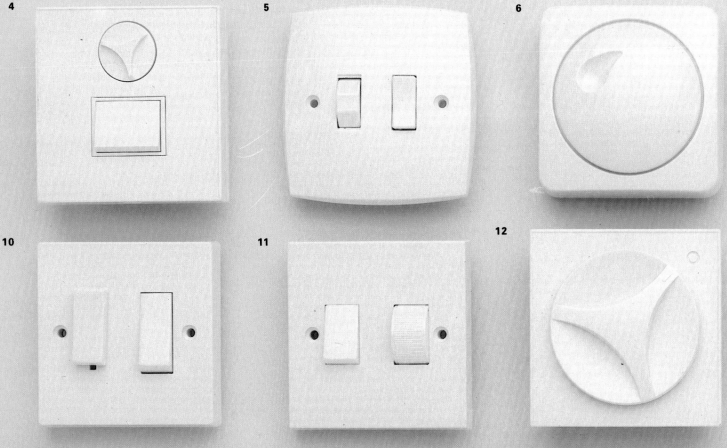

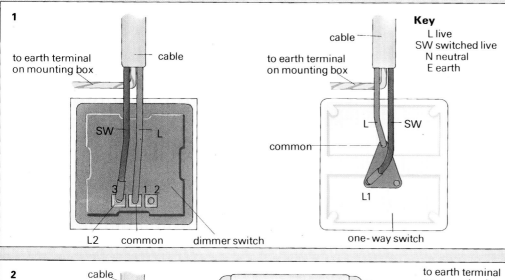

1

to earth terminal
on mounting box — cable

SW   L

3   1 2

L2   common   dimmer switch

cable

to earth terminal
on mounting box

L — SW

common

L1

one- way switch

Key
L live
SW switched live
N neutral
E earth

3

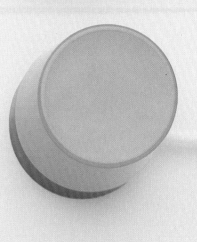

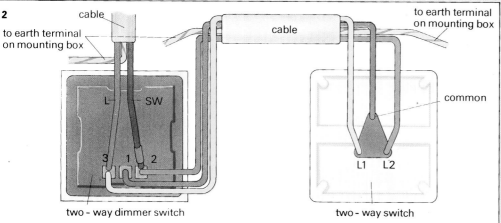

2

cable

to earth terminal
on mounting box

L — SW

3   1   2

two - way dimmer switch

cable

to earth terminal
on mounting box

common

L1   L2

two - way switch

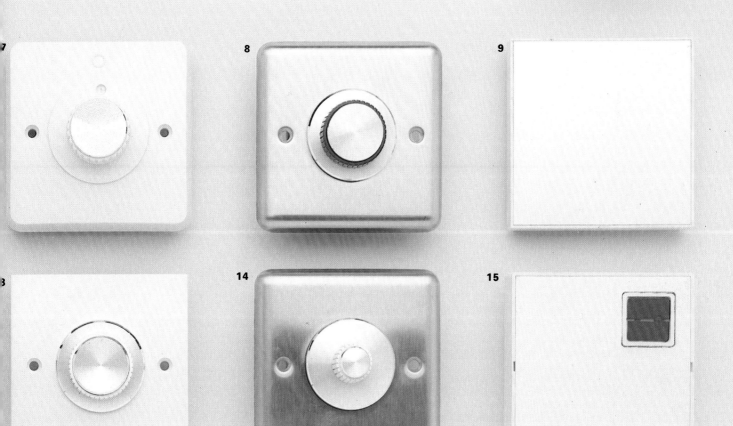

7

8

9

3

14

15

on-off switch can be used to replace any existing two-gang switch unit to provide the facility for dimming some lighting in a room, while using the rest of the lighting at a fixed intensity. In a dining/living room, for example, you can have a rise-and-fall pendant over the dining table under dimmer control, while the centre light, wall lights or spotlights may be at fixed intensity, or vice versa.

There is a more expensive unit available which provides dimming facilities on two different sets of lighting and, like all the other dimmers, requires no alteration to the wiring when replacing a conventional switch, in this case a two gang switch.

Table lamp dimmer

Table or standard lamps may be put under dimmer control by fitting a lampholder adaptor. You simply remove the lamp, fit the dimmer in its place and insert the lamp in the dimmer lampholder. Intensity is controlled by a knob on the side of the dimmer.

Another version is available in the form of a plug adaptor. This is either connected to the flex of the portable lamp or has its own pins to connect with a socket outlet and has a socket of its own into which the lamp is connected.

Armchair or bedside dimming is possible with a portable dimmer switch, which is sold in either white or orange and has a black weighted base. The dimmer is controlled by rotating the top and slight downward pressure switches the light on or off. The control unit is connected by a flexible cord to a socket adaptor, into which the portable lamp is plugged.

Touch dimmer

The most recent type available is the touch dimmer, which is operated when a gentle touch on a small touch pad, fitted flush into the switch plate, operates the dimming and/or switching. These dimmers all fit standard square flush-mounted metal boxes.

One touch on the pad dims the light; repeated tapping varies the dimming until the desired level is reached. There are separate touch pads for changing the light level up and down and the unit has a memory which restores the light level after a power cut. These dimmers, which contain a fuse to protect the circuitry, must not be fitted into a two-way circuit.

Master touch dimmer

Another version of the touch dimmer enables dimming to be controlled from more than one switching position. For two-way switching, a master touch dimmer is fitted in place of a switch at one position and a slave dimmer at the second point or each point on an intermediate switching circuit. The master has a neon indicator.

Dimmer switch failure

Dimmers should be chosen and treated carefully because they contain delicate components. Never exceed the watts rating. Low-priced equipment with ratings of only 200 watts are satisfactory for simple light fittings; but if you are likely to install a multi-light fitting at a later date, it is better to fit a dimmer in the 400–500 watts range. This also applies to wall lights when there is a chance that more powerful replacement bulbs will be fitted later on.

If a dimmer is overloaded it will almost certainly fail. Dimmer failure is sometimes caused by failure

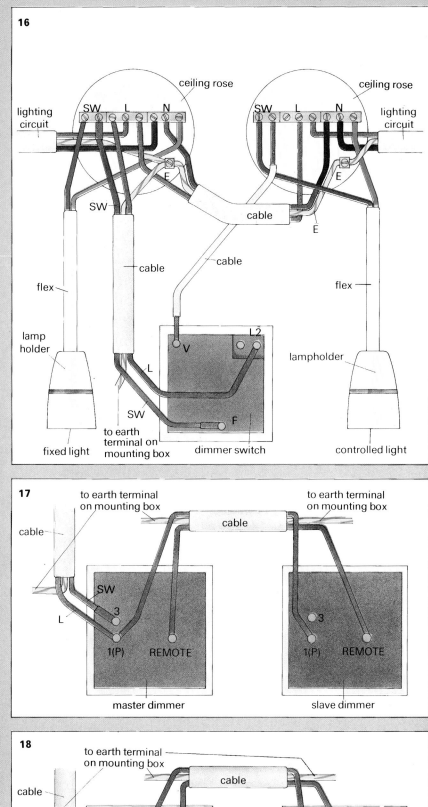

16 fixed light / dimmer switch / controlled light

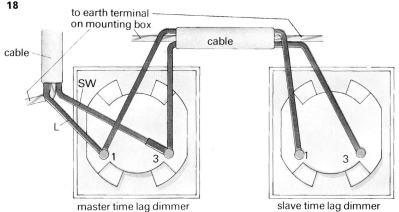

17 master dimmer / slave dimmer

18 master time lag dimmer / slave time lag dimmer

of a light bulb when a surge of heavy current flows in the circuit and through the dimmer: this short circuit can exist long enough to destroy the semiconductor. To eliminate these risks, manufacturers are beginning to introduce small sand-filled cartridge fuses – similar to, but smaller than, a 13amp plug fuse – into their dimmer switches.

Types of time switch

The conventional vacuum-operated time lag switch – used with stair and corridor lighting to save electricity – will operate for up to five minutes, but can be dangerous to stair users because it gives no warning before cutting out. The control, which can also be fitted in place of any square-plate switch, comes in a touch pad version.

However the most up-to-date version is a device which incorporates a time lag control with the touch pad facility but maintains a degree of light; the light does not cut out, but fades and then holds indefinitely at a safety level. A slight touch will then turn off the light electronically. This is also a standard square-plate switch and can replace any one-way switch without wiring modifications.

Also available is a master time lag dimmer of the touch pad type which can be used in a two-way or intermediate switching circuit. It is fitted in place of one of the two-way switches (or intermediate switches in a multi-switching circuit) and the other remains as an ordinary switch; but it also operates the light or lights and begins the time lag sequence.

Burglar deterrent switches

Leaving lights on in a house may deter a casual would-be intruder, but it is unlikely to fool a professional house-breaker. Deterrent lighting should be switched on and off at the proper time and solar-operated devices, which go on at sundown and off at sunrise, are available.

One of the most useful for the home is a dimmer switch fitted with a photo cell which enables the light to be left on at a low level and therefore is not expensive to run. This can be used to replace any modern square-plate one-way or two-way switch without modification to the wiring.

Another type of burglar deterrent is the combined on-off time switch which operates as an ordinary switch and can be set to turn lights on or off automatically at frequent intervals to give the impression the house is being used. Bear in mind, house-breakers know which rooms are used when.

16 Wiring dimmer switch to provide both fixed and controlled light in same room
17 Wiring master dimmer to slave
18 Wiring master time lag dimmer to slave
19 Slimline time switch with socket outlet, override switch and facility for two on/off switchings in 24 hours
20 Time switch with socket outlet, override switch and facility for one or two on/off switchings in 24 hours
21 Time switch with socket outlet, override switch and facility for hourly on/off switching

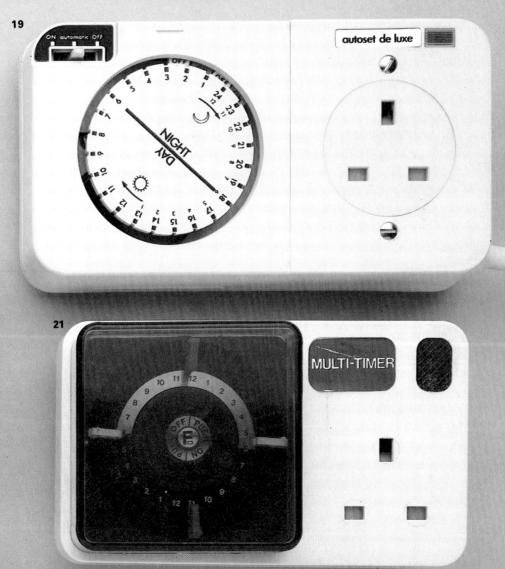

Installing spot and wall lights

Wall-mounted lights and spotlights offer wide scope for lighting arrangements since they can be installed in any room as the main lighting or to supplement existing lighting, which is usually supplied by a conventional ceiling rose. If you have individual lighting, such as a rise and fall pendant over the dining table, wall lights can be used to provide general illumination.

Spotlights are particularly versatile since they can be fitted on the wall or the ceiling and can be used to highlight particular features of the room such as pictures, displays or even curtains. Spotlights are particularly useful for providing local lighting for reading, sewing and other similar activities since they are available with swivel brackets which allow the light to be directed as required. Wall lights or spotlights are also very useful in a double bedroom since light can be localized, causing the minimum disturbance to the other occupant.

Types of lamp Spotlights use two principal kinds of lamps: a reflector lamp of 75 watts is available in clear (white), blue, green, red and yellow; the PAR 38 sealed beam spotlight and floodlight (100 and 150 watts) is available in the same range of colours. The latter is suitable for both indoor and outdoor use, the floodlight version giving a wider beam of light suitable for illuminating outdoor areas. When buying fittings for spotlights, check which size and type of lamp it will accept; on some models the wattage is stamped inside the holder.

Fittings These are usually made of either polished or matt aluminium or finished in enamel in a variety of colours including white and pastel shades of green, yellow and mauve. Lighting track is particularly useful for holding spotlights. Available in various lengths, this can be fixed to the ceiling or wall and will take a number of spotlights which can be locked in position on the track.

Wiring wall lights

New wall lights may well need wiring extensions from the existing circuit, unless you are fortunate enough to move into a new home where wall lights have already been installed by previous owners or decide to fit wall lights with a flexible cord from a plug and socket outlet. In the case of new circuit wiring, the power may be run from three sources – from an existing lighting circuit, from a ring circuit via a fused connection unit or from a new lighting circuit in the consumer unit.

The lights are usually added to the circuit supplying the same floor, although there is much to be said for using a different circuit – from another floor, if it is a two-storey house, or from a circuit supplying other rooms, if a bungalow. A different circuit will mean the lights in the room will be supplied from more than one circuit, preventing a blackout should a fuse blow. This will also ease pressure on the ground floor or main living area lighting circuit, which tends to become overloaded if extra lights are added. There are regulations covering the maximum number of lights on one circuit – 12 lamps not more than 100 watts each on one circuit and fewer when one or more 150 watt lamps are fitted. Where added wall lights – especially those having two lamps, even if they are only 40 or 60 watts – will exceed the regulation number, use another circuit or install a new circuit, which can be a fused spur from a ring main.

Wiring from existing circuits Although wall lights are more conveniently controlled independently from the other lighting, wiring can be simplified by connecting to the existing fittings and using the existing light switch by the door. In this case the wall lights should have their own switches so they may be turned off if you want just a main light.

1 Screw cap crown-silvered spotlamp
2 Bayonet cap reflector spotlamp
3 Screw cap reflector spotlamp
4 Dual box
5 Bayonet cap reflector spot lamp
6 Screw cap sealed beam PAR 38 lamp
7 BESA box with brass bush
8 Architrave box

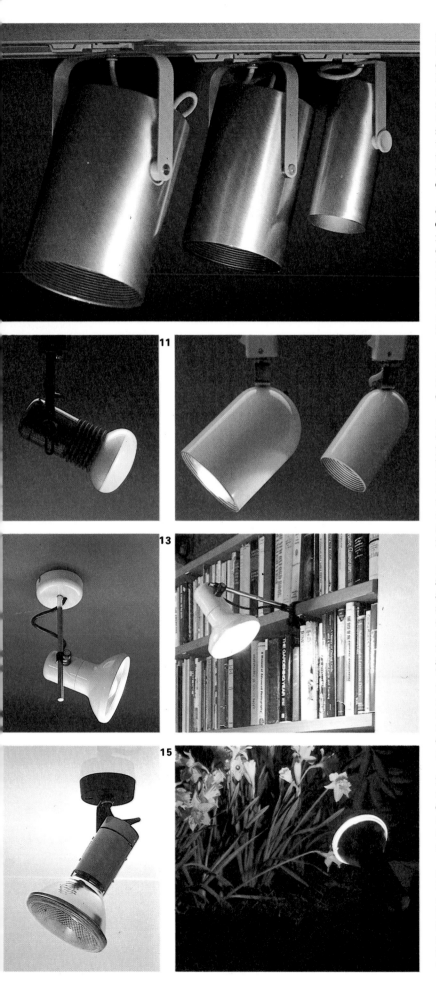

The problem with this arrangement is that to have the wall lights on you must also have the main light on. This can be overcome either by fixing a cord-operated ceiling switch or by replacing the lampholder in the ceiling with a switched version, if it has an open shade. A more satisfactory solution is to connect to the neutral terminal on the existing light and replace the existing one gang switch with a two gang switch; the second switch will be for the wall lights. Mount the new switch on the same box and use the existing unswitched live to supply both switches. This technique has been covered earlier in the book.

Where, however, the existing circuit is wired on the loop-in ceiling rose system, as most modern circuits are, there will be a live terminal as well as a neutral one at the rose; this is the ideal source of electricity for the wall light circuit. If not wired on the loop-in system and if the ceiling light switch is located in the wrong part of the room, it will be necessary either to locate a junction box on the lighting circuit to allow access to a live terminal or to run a cable from the lighting circuit fuseway in the consumer unit.

Whichever method you use to obtain the source of electricity, you will need a four terminal 15/20amp plastic junction box – the basic accessory for the wiring – and flat 1.0sq mm twin core and earth, PVC sheathed cable.

The junction box is fixed under the floor to a piece of timber between the joists, roughly equidistant from the wall lights and the wall switch position. A convenient position for the box is above the existing ceiling light, if the light is used for looping. Run a length of cable from the junction box to each wall light, preferably a separate cable to each. This will save you having to run two cables down the wall to all but the last wall light, and having to house two cables and the connectors in the confined space behind the backplate.

Run a cable from the junction box to the switch position; if this is the same as the existing switch, a two gang unit replaces the one gang switch. Run a final cable from the junction box to the source of supply – the ceiling lighting point, a junction box or the consumer unit. When making the connections at the junction box, ensure the ends of the sheathing terminate within the box and all earth conductors are enclosed in green/yellow PVC sheathing.

Wiring from ring circuit In this case it is necessary to insert a fused connection unit into the 30amp ring main and fit a 3amp fuse in the unit to protect the lighting wiring, which has a lower current rating. The simplest method is to loop out of a convenient 13amp socket outlet connected to the ring cable and not fed from a spur cable.

The socket outlet you choose should be on the first floor, if in a two-storey house, so cable may be run under the floorboards; this will save having cable running up walls and will also normally mean the lights are on a different circuit than, for example, table lamps, which will be on the ring circuit in the ground floor rooms.

Turn the power off and remove a socket outlet to check it is not a spur, as described earlier in the book. A single socket box can be replaced by a dual box which is slightly longer than a two gang box and has two extra screw-fixing lugs for mounting two single accessories side by side (in this instance one will be the fused connection unit). If connecting the fused connection unit to a double socket, you will need a separate single box for the unit alongside the socket box. The fused connection unit must be connected to the socket outlet terminals by 2.5sq mm twin core and earth PVC-sheathed cable.

From the fused connection unit run a length of 1.0sq mm twin core and earth PVC-sheathed cable to the junction box feeding the wall lights and switch. Connect the 2.5sq mm cable to the mains terminals of the fused connection unit and the 1.0sq mm cable to the load terminals.

9 Track-mounted spotlights. **10** Track-mounted spot with reflector lamp. **11** Track-mounted spots. **12** Spotlight for wall or ceiling mounting. **13** Clamp-on fitting. **14** Sealed beam spot for wall or ceiling mounting. **15** Outdoor sealed beam spot. **16** Wiring a cord-operated switch to a ceiling light. **17a** The wiring system for the existing junction box and ceiling rose. **17b** Wiring a two gang switch from the junction box system. **17c** Wiring a separate switch from the junction box system

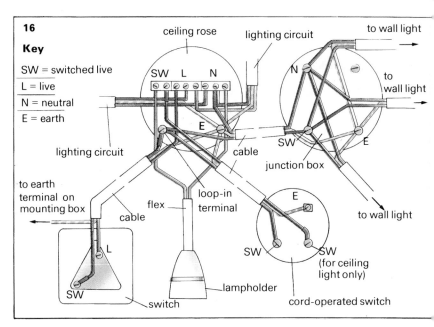

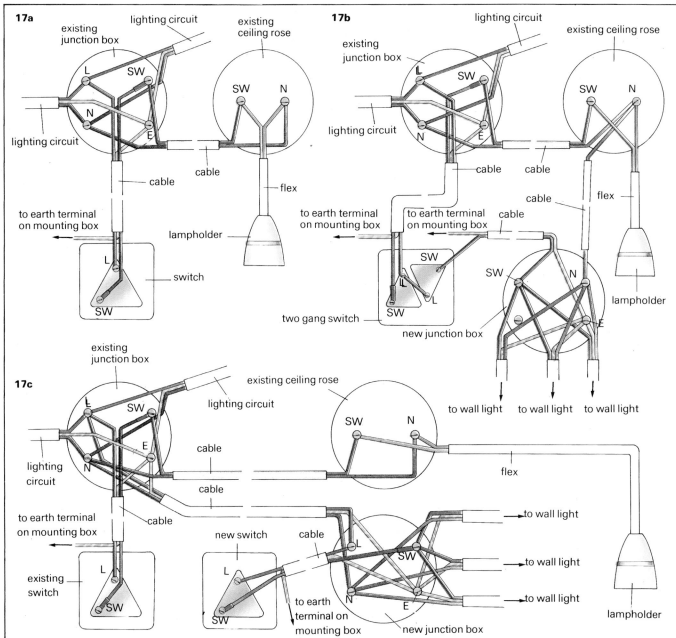

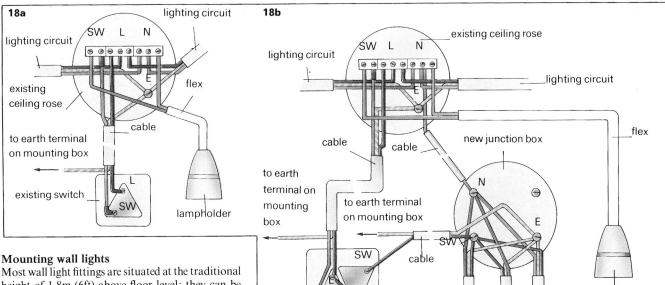

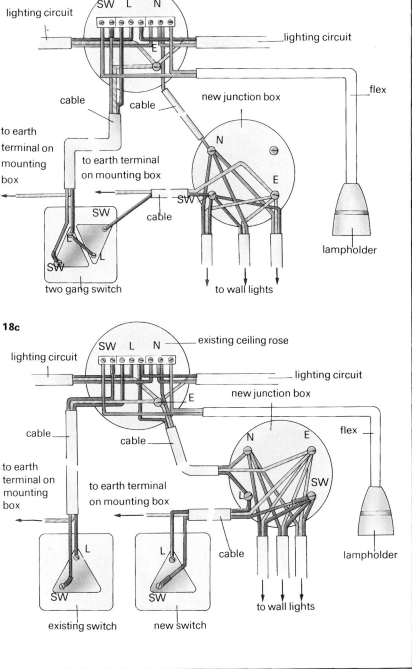

Mounting wall lights

Most wall light fittings are situated at the traditional height of 1.8m (6ft) above floor level; they can be fitted at any preferred height, depending upon the height of the ceiling and the style of the fitting.

Usually they have a backplate or base which has an open back. Regulations require the ends of cables, cable connectors and fitting flex to be totally enclosed in non-combustible material; a plastic or metal box is usually sunk into the wall and covered by the backplate of the fitting. Often the wall lights will have a circular backplate with two fixing holes drilled at 50mm (2in) fixing centres which match the standard 'BS' circular conduit box (termed BESA).

A plastic box can be used for all but very heavy fittings. If a metal box is used, fit a male brass bush into the threaded conduit entry in the edge to prevent the cable chafing as it enters the box. The metal version is also used for lights having a rectangular backplate with drilled fixings, made of wood, metal or plastic. Many wall lights, however, have no BESA plate and some are very narrow and of shapes unsuited to the BESA box. These require a narrow metal knock-out box (half the width of a socket outlet box) called an architrave box and designed for use with an architrave plateswitch. Remove the knock-out disc from the box and fit a PVC grommet to protect the cable.

The box is sunk into a chase cut into the wall, fixed with screws in plugged holes. Thread in the circuit cable, dropping it down from the ceiling; the cable may be clipped to the wall or buried in the plaster as desired. Trim and prepare the end of the cable in each box by stripping off the sheathing down to about 19mm ($\frac{3}{4}$in) and remove about 9mm ($\frac{3}{8}$in) of insulation from the two insulated conductors; slip green/yellow PVC sleeving over the bare end of the earth conductor. Using a two way insulated cable connector (already connected to the fitting wires in some wall light fittings), connect the red circuit wire to the brown wire of the fitting, the black to the blue and the earth wire of each to the earth terminal in the box. If there is no earth terminal, as in a plastic box, terminate the earth with a one way cable connector.

With a BESA box, secure the fitting to the box lugs with M.4 metric (2BA) screws (usually supplied). With an architrave box, the fitting can be fixed directly to the wall using screws in plugged holes. Should one of the fixing holes coincide with the box, it will be necessary to fix a drilled metal cover to the box using M3.5 metric (4BA) screws; drill another hole in the cover for a self-tapping

screw to hold the fitting. Run cable down to the switch and fit as described earlier in the book. Check the power is still turned off and connect the cable to the existing ceiling fitting, junction box or fuseway as relevant.

Mounting spotlights

Spotlights can be mounted at any height on a wall or in any position on a ceiling. Wiring is the same as for wall lights, except when the spotlights are to be ceiling-mounted; here a cable is passed through a hole pierced in the ceiling as for a conventional ceiling rose.

Most spotlight fittings have a circular base drilled for 50mm (2in) fixings and are therefore suitable for mounting on a BESA box. Many are sold ready wired with a short length of three core

18a Existing loop-in ceiling rose system. **18b** Wiring a two gang switch from the loop-in system. **18c** Wiring a separate switch from the loop-in system. **19a** Wiring a new circuit from the consumer unit. **19b** Wiring a new circuit from a ring circuit. **20a** Mounting a wall light on a BESA box. **20b** Mounting a wall light on an architrave box; where it cannot be screwed both sides of the box, fit a metal cover and hold the fitting with a self-tapping screw

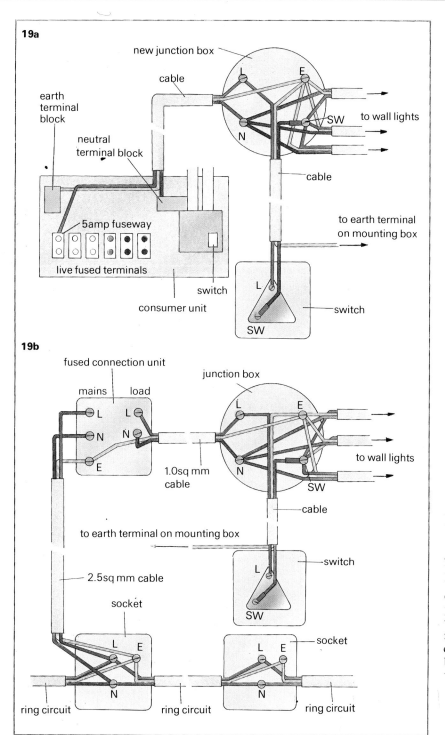

19a

new junction box

cable

earth terminal block

neutral terminal block

5amp fuseway

live fused terminals

consumer unit

switch

L

E

SW   to wall lights

N

cable

to earth terminal on mounting box

L

SW

switch

19b

fused connection unit

mains   load

L   L

N   N

E

1.0sq mm cable

junction box

L   E

SW   to wall lights

N

cable

to earth terminal on mounting box

2.5sq mm cable

socket

L   E

N

ring circuit

ring circuit

switch

L

SW

socket

L   E

N

ring circuit

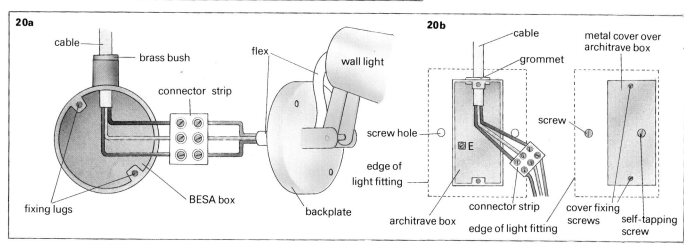

20a

cable

brass bush

connector strip

flex

wall light

fixing lugs

BESA box

backplate

20b

cable

grommet

metal cover over architrave box

screw

screw hole

E

edge of light fitting

connector strip

architrave box

cover fixing screws

edge of light fitting

self-tapping screw

circular sheathed flex passing out through a small hole in the baseplate edge. This means instead of being mounted over a BESA box, the base can be fixed directly to the wall and the flex connected to a plug and socket outlet, ceiling rose or switched fused connection unit.

Lighting tracks enable one or more spotlights to be mounted in line on a ceiling or wall. Lighting pendants and the occasional small appliance may also be plugged into a lighting track. Domestic tracks come in standard lengths and couplers enable you to extend the track to any length. The tracks have a current rating of 16amps, although in practice the load is limited to the current rating of the circuit feeding the track. From a 5amp circuit the limit is 1200 watts; from a 3amp fused spur it is 720 watts; from a 13amp fused spur up to 3120 watts may be run off. The last is necessary if a large number of high-powered spotlights are to be connected to the track.

A lighting track is basically a PVC extrusion containing two bare conductors (live and neutral) with an earth strip, enclosed in an anodized aluminium track. Spotlights fitted with track adaptors clip into the track and will slide along until locked into position. Flexible cord adaptors may be fitted to the track to operate a lighting pendant or an appliance fitted with the adaptor in place of a conventional plug. A cord-operated 2amp switch to control up to 480 watts is available, which may be clipped into the track if required. A track can be connected directly to fixed wiring either at a wall lighting point or at a ceiling point in place of a ceiling rose and operated by conventional wall switches. Alternatively flexible cord can be connected to the track terminals, which in turn are connected to a ceiling rose, cord outlet or to a plug and socket outlet.

Warning Every spotlight and wall light must be under the control of an isolating switch, such as a conventional wall switch, even when the fittings have their own integral switches. This is to ensure the lampholder and other live parts are dead whenever you attend to the fitting. A cord-operated, or push-button, integral switch does not indicate whether the fitting is on or off. Spotlights are made in the 100–150 watt range, so check the lighting circuit will not be overloaded; if the circuit would be overloaded, a ring circuit spur should be used to supply the power.

Fitting a new consumer unit

There is nothing more aggravating than wanting to add new electrical equipment in the home and not being able to include a new circuit to supply it. You may find you need to install a larger consumer unit than the one already fitted in order to cope with this, which is a job you can do yourself.

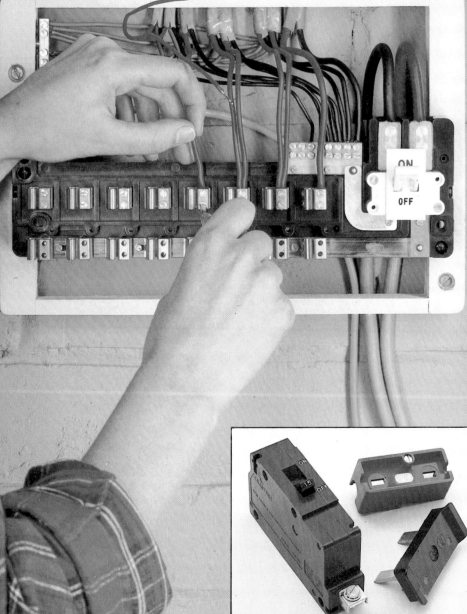

The final stage of wiring up a new consumer unit **Inset** Check whether your unit has miniature circuit breakers (**left**) or fuse carriers (**right**)

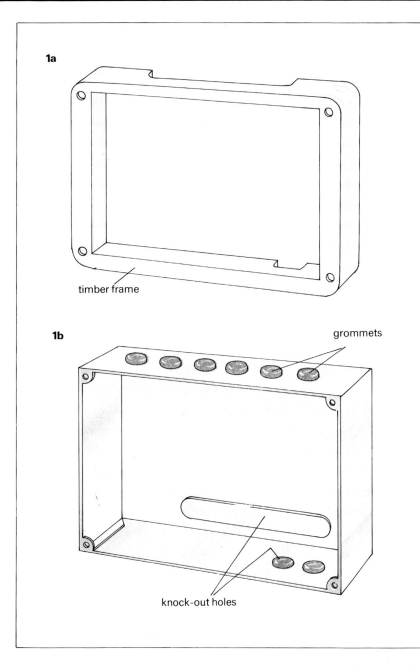

1a

timber frame

1b

grommets

knock-out holes

2

LIGHTING ①

LIGHTING ②

IMMERSION HEATER

RING CIRCUIT ①

RING CIRCUIT ②

COOKER

adhesive tape

A consumer unit is a comparatively modern piece of electrical equipment which combines the necessary double pole main switch with a single pole fuseboard in one casing. It should be situated as close as possible to the Electricity Board meter, to which it is connected by the meter tails which provide the supply. The switch is double pole so both the live and the neutral supplies are cut off simultaneously when the main switch is turned off. The fuses in the consumer unit, which protect individual circuits and equipment from excess current caused by a fault or overloading, interrupt the current in the live circuit.

Deciding number of circuits

The size of consumer units varies from two-way, for an installation with only two-circuits, to 12-way; the most common unit installed in a home is eight-way. Generally the size is determined by the number of circuits involved when the house is built. So when an additional circuit is required, perhaps for a shower heater or power point in your garage, there is no spare fuseway. As the

wiring regulations do not permit any fuse to supply more than one circuit, you have two alternatives: either fit a main switch and fuse unit next to the consumer unit or replace the unit with a larger one with more fuses. A separate switch and fuse unit needs a separate mains connection and since Electricity Boards will not allow more than one pair of leads connected to their meter, a special terminal box has to be fitted on the consumer's side of the installation. Such a unit can provide one, two or four extra circuits. It is more satisfactory to replace the consumer unit and normally it is a waste of time and money to fit one smaller than an eight-way; this will, for example, supply two lighting circuits, two ring circuits, a cooker, an immersion heater and leave two spare fuseways for future expansion.

Choosing unit

There are three principal types: one with fuses that can be rewired or fitted with cartridge fuses, another fitted with miniature circuit breakers (mcb) and a third which accepts either fuses or mcbs. The circuit breakers give the best protection, while cartridge fuses are next best; most units have wire fuses because they are cheapest. New consumer units now often incorporate mcbs and an RCD (residual current device) – see page 279.

The current required to blow a wire fuse is twice the rating of the fuse, which means a 10amp current is required to blow a 5amp fuse. A cartridge blows at one and a half times its rated current and an mcb operates when only one and a quarter times its rated current flows in the circuit. An mcb also operates much quicker than a fuse and reduces the risk of fire or damage to the circuit or appliance. If price is a consideration, it is worth remembering an mcb costs about three times as much as a fused unit. You do not repair an mcb; you simply press a button or turn on a switch to reactivate it – as long as you have dealt with the problem that caused it to break the circuit. Fuse wires and cartridges must be replaced and it is vital to keep spares.

Five ratings Circuit fuses and mcbs are made in five ratings, each with a different colour code, for domestic use: 5 (white), 15 (blue), 20 (yellow), 30 (red) and 45 (green). Consumer units do not usually have provision for a 45amp fuseway, which occu-

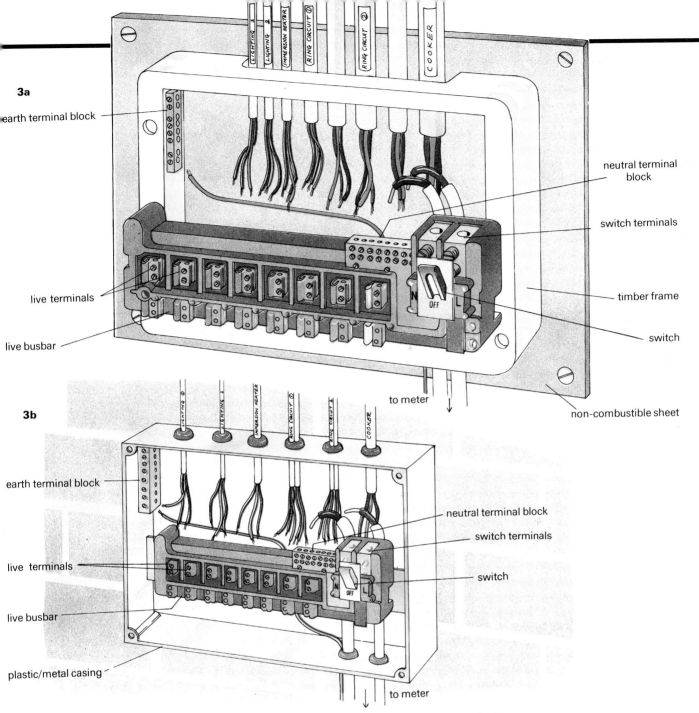

3a

earth terminal block

LIGHTING 1
LIGHTING 2
IMMERSION HEATER
RING CIRCUIT 1
RING CIRCUIT 2
COOKER

neutral terminal block

switch terminals

live terminals

live busbar

timber frame

switch

to meter

non-combustible sheet

3b

earth terminal block

LIGHTING 2
LIGHTING 1
IMMERSION HEATER
RING CIRCUIT 2
RING CIRCUIT 1
COOKER

neutral terminal block

switch terminals

live terminals

switch

live busbar

plastic/metal casing

to meter

1a Recesses for meter leads in timber frame of plastic consumer unit
1b Knock-out holes for circuit cables in all-metal – or plastic – units. (Terminals are omitted in these diagrams)
2 Labelling cables and taping ring circuit cables together
3a Feeding cables into plastic/timber frame unit
3b Feeding cables into all-metal – or plastic – unit

pies the space of two standard fuseways in some units and is needed only for a circuit supplying, for example, a large cooker with a loading of 17kW or more. If you are changing your existing unit for a larger installation, you will probably find your present fuses or mcbs will be suitable for your new unit and will save you some expense.

Disconnecting mains
Before you remove your existing consumer unit or fuseboard, the power must be disconnected at the mains by the withdrawal of the service fuse and you must give your Electricity Board at least 48 hours' notice, in writing, that you require a temporary disconnection.

Electricity Boards are obliged by law to isolate a consumer's installation from the mains on request during normal working hours.

You can usually make the change in one day and if electricity is disconnected at 9am you can have the supply restored at 5pm. If by midday you realize you cannot complete the job in time, you can always ask for reconnection to be postponed.

Preparing for installation
Some preparatory work can be done a day or so before you have the electricity cut off. Check you have all the materials and equipment you require. Remove the cover from the new unit and the fuses or mcbs, if they are bought already fitted. This leaves only the main switch, terminal banks and the copper busbar to which the fuse units are screwed. Consumer units are made entirely in metal, or plastic, or a plastic casing with a timber frame. The metal and all-plastic units have knock-out holes at the top and bottom and at the back. If it is a plastic case on a timber frame, you should either drill holes or cut recesses for the cables in the timber frame (at the top or bottom or both, depending on whether your circuit cables run up from ground level or down from ceiling height); if the cables are channelled into the plaster, they can be brought into the unit through the back of the timber frame. If the unit is to be mounted on a combustible material a sheet of non-combustible material should be fixed between the unit and the wall.
Strip cable Strip about 50mm (2in) of sheathing

4

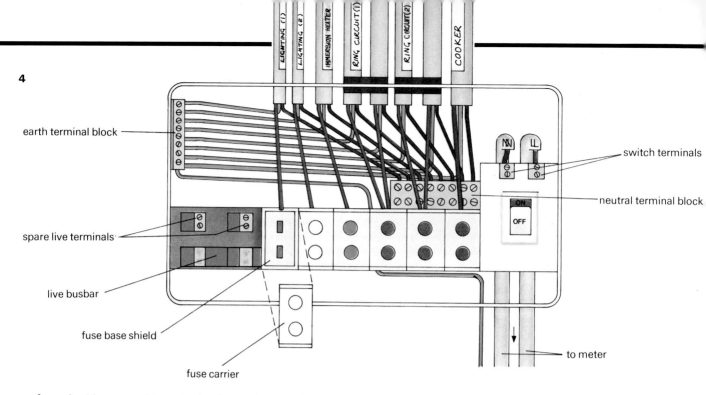

earth terminal block

switch terminals

neutral terminal block

spare live terminals

live busbar

fuse base shield

fuse carrier

to meter

from the 16sq mm cable and take about 13mm
(½in) of insulation off each conductor. Connect the
red (live) conductor to the L terminal and the black
(neutral) conductor to the N terminal. Tighten the
screws and replace the insulated sleeves, where
fitted. Make sure you have enough cable for the
Electricity Board official to connect up. Your
existing earthing lead should be connected to the
earthing terminal on your new unit after the supply
has been disconnected. If you are fitting a new
earthing lead, you can fit it to the earthing terminal but don't connect it to earth; the Electricity
Board official will do that.

Check all the circuits are labelled on the existing
consumer unit. If not, by switching on all lights and
appliances and then withdrawing fuses one by one,
turning off the mains switch before pulling out each
fuse, you can identify the circuits. Label them by
attaching self-adhesive stickers on the cover of the
consumer unit and then prepare a second set of
labels which will go on the cables.

Changing over
When the electricity has been cut off, take off the
cover from the existing consumer unit and remove
the fuses. Loosen the terminal screws on each fuse
holder in turn and disconnect the live circuit wires,
which should all be red. As you disconnect, wrap
the appropriate identification label round each
circuit cable. Where two cables were connected to
one fuseway in a ring circuit, use a piece of adhesive
tape to bind them together until you reconnect to
the new unit. Release the wires from the neutral and
earthing terminals. Remove the frame or casing of
the unit, replaster any holes and make good any
decoration as required.
Fixing unit Take the frame, or casing, of the new
unit, hold it in position on the wall and mark the
fixing holes. Drill and plug the holes and screw the
unit into position. Don't forget to fix a non-
combustible sheet between the unit and the wall
if you are mounting on a combustible material.
Feed the circuit cables into the casing and connect
them to the fuseways (an mcb unit may require
the mcbs to be positioned first). Starting at
the main switch end of the unit, connect your
cooker circuit (if you have one) or the first of your

ring main circuits. Connect the red conductor to
the first live terminal, the black to the first terminal
on the neutral bank and, after fitting some green/
yellow PVC sleeving if none is present, connect
the bare earth conductor to the first earthing
terminal. The end of the cable sheathing must be
within the case or the frame. Continue to connect
up in descending order of rating: 30, 20, 15 and 5.
Any spare fuseways must be fitted with blanking
plates until required. The circuits should, ideally, be
rearranged where necessary when the current
rating of any new circuit is known.

Fitting fuse bases
Screw the fuse bases – they are sometimes called
shields – into their correct position according to
their rating on the live busbar. This is important
because it would be dangerous, for instance, to fit
a 30amp base and fuse carrier to a 5amp circuit.
The fuse bases and carriers are sold together, so
when you buy your new equipment you must know
exactly what your circuit ratings will be. The bases
are manufactured to accept only a carrier of their
own rating (or sometimes smaller) – you can
never fit a 15amp fuse carrier into a 5amp base and
so on. The colour coding of bases and carriers helps
to eliminate mistakes and aids quick identification
when you are changing a fuse wire or a cartridge if
a circuit blows. When the bases are installed, replace
the terminal cover if there is one and insert the
fuse carriers. Finally replace the fuse cover (having
taken care to identify the circuits with adhesive
labels inside the cover) and wait for the electricity
man to call to reconnect you. It is unlikely he will
test your work unless new circuits have been added
at the same time as you installed the new consumer
unit: but the decision is his and you must be prepared for him to check out the work.
Earth sleeving Until recently sleeving on earth
wires was always green in colour; this has now been
standardized to green/yellow, although you are
still likely to come across the old sleeving, particularly in older houses.

4 Circuit cables wired up
correctly into new
consumer unit

42

Residual current devices

A residual current device (known as an RCD) is a double pole mains switch which automatically trips (switches off) when there is sufficient leakage of current from a live wire or earth terminal to earth. It does not normally operate, however, when a circuit is overloaded or if it develops a short circuit (when the live and neutral wires are in contact with each other. RCDs used to be known as earth leakage circuit breakers (ELCBs); the term is retained here because it is more familiar.

The ELCB is used as an alternative or back-up device for earthing; in other words it is used where earthing is likely to be poor or ineffective. It is fitted with a tripping coil which is energized by current leaking to earth through it or in some part of the installation, producing an out-of-balance current in the circuit breaker. When the tripping coil is energized, an electro-magnet lifts a latch and releases the switch mechanism which is operated by a powerful spring. On release, the switch contacts open and the circuits and/or faulty apparatus are isolated from the mains electricity.

The current required to energize the trip coil is a tiny portion of the current flowing through the circuit breakers under normal conditions. By cutting off the current to a circuit when there is an earth leakage, the ELCB does the work of a fuse – but with much less current and with greater speed. For example, a 30amp rewireable fuse (the largest in most homes) requires 60amps to blow it; a 30amp cartridge fuse requires 45amps and a 30amp miniature circuit breaker (MCB) requires 37amps. The large currents required to cut off the supply when there is an earth leakage put great strain on the circuit wiring and a very good earthing system is needed if the fuse is to blow or the MCB is to operate. But a modern ELCB needs less than 1 amp to operate, so the fuses and any MCBs remain intact since the ELCB trips off instead.

How it works

An earth leakage current returns to the electricity supply system, usually at the substation which might be some distance from the house. But instead of returning through the neutral conductor, as current does in its normal state, it has to follow an alternative path. Originally the faulty current left the house through the mains water pipe, through the mains water network and onto the substation. Because water authorities are now using insulated pipes, the mains water system may no longer be used as the sole means of earthing in new or existing installations. Now the metallic sheathing of the Electricity Board's cable provides a continuous metallic path for the earth leakage current back to the substation. In some areas the Electricity Board also offers another system known as protective multiple earthing (PME). This takes advantage of the fact that the neutral pole of the mains electricity is solidly connected to earth at the substation and gives a first class earthing system.

Earthing terminal The Electricity Board sometimes provides a terminal in the house for earth connection, for which it may make a small charge. Where the Board is unable to provide an earth terminal – either because the metallic sheathing is not continuous or because PME has not been adopted in the area – the consumer must find an alternative, since he is responsible for earthing.

For direct connection of an earthing circuit to earth, the impedance (AC equivalent of DC resistance) of the earth connection must not exceed 4 ohms to enable it to carry the 60amp or more current which may result from a leakage. Earth terminals provided by the Electricity Board meet these requirements; but alternative systems provided by the consumer are unlikely to do so. For example, simply installing an electrode in the ground to provide an earth terminal would result in fuses failing to blow should an earth leakage fault occur; the installation would be dangerous with a high fire and electrocution risk. The solution here would be to install an earth leakage circuit breaker in conjunction with an earth electrode.

Installing earth electrode The copper or copper-sheathed electrode must be a minimum of 1200mm (or 48in) long and it should be driven vertically into firm soil so the clamp terminal is just above ground level. Firm soil is essential to provide good electrical conductivity between the electrode rod and earth; the moisture content of the subsoil will further improve conductivity. When deciding on a suitable position for the electrode, bear in mind the concrete foundations of a house wall are probably not more than 300mm (or 12in) below ground level and they protrude between 75 and 100mm (3 and 4in) beyond the faces of the wall. If your consumer unit is situated in a cellar, you can drill a hole – larger than the electrode – in the wall, drive the electrode horizontally through this into the subsoil and seal around it with mastic; or drill a hole in the floor and insert the rod, but in either case beware of the presence of a damp proof membrane which would be punctured by this process and

Above Voltage-operated ELCB
Left Current-operated high sensitivity ELCB
Below Earth electrode

> **WARNING**
> **You should consult the Electricity Board before undertaking any protective installation since there are now new regulations on earthing circuits.**

ON

CRABTREE

TYPE PS60 ELCB
         40A

415V 3Ph 50Hz
30mA RATED TRIP

Test often using Button T

OFF

CMC–SWISS MADE

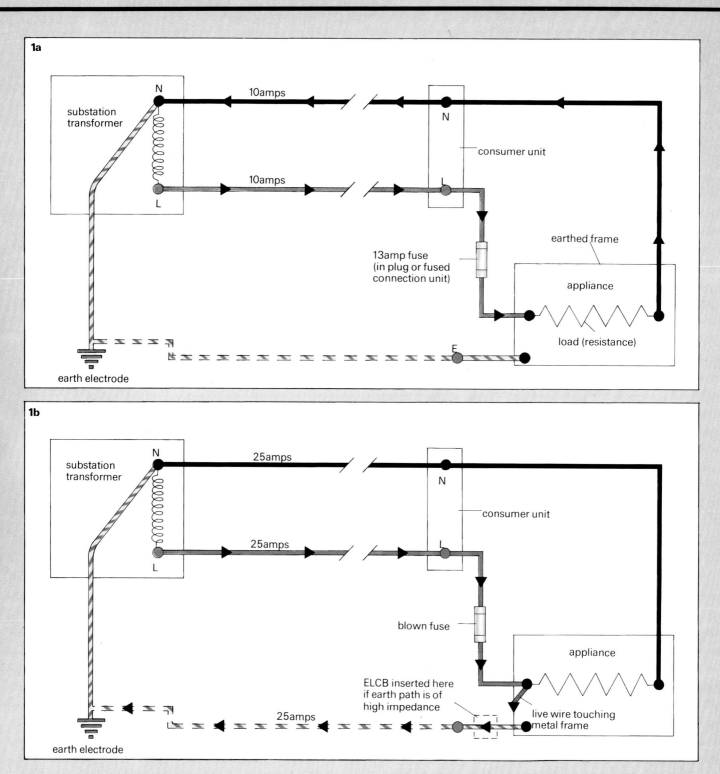

1a

substation transformer

N

10amps

consumer unit

N

10amps

L

13amp fuse
(in plug or fused
connection unit)

earthed frame

appliance

load (resistance)

E

earth electrode

1b

substation transformer

N

25amps

consumer unit

N

25amps

L

blown fuse

appliance

ELCB inserted here
if earth path is of
high impedance

live wire touching
metal frame

25amps

earth electrode

allow damp to penetrate. Connection to the terminal clamp should be with 6 or 10sq mm single core green/yellow PVC-insulated cable; at the connection point fix an indelible label stating: 'Safety Electrical Earth – Do Not Remove'.

Types of ELCB
There are two main types of ELCB installed in the home: one is voltage-operated and the other current-operated. The current-operated ELCB

should be your first choice, but if the product of the operating current and the impedance of the earth loop (as measured on an impedance tester by the Electricity Board or an electrical contractor) exceeds 50, you must use the voltage-operated type.
Voltage-operated This is the cheapest ELCB and is simply a double pole circuit breaker with trip coil and tripping mechanism. The circuit breaker section has four main terminals – a conventional double pole mains switch and two subsidiary

1a The normal current path from the substation to an appliance via the consumer unit
1b The current path where current from a short circuit, caused by the live wire in an appliance touching an earthed frame, returns to the substation via earth

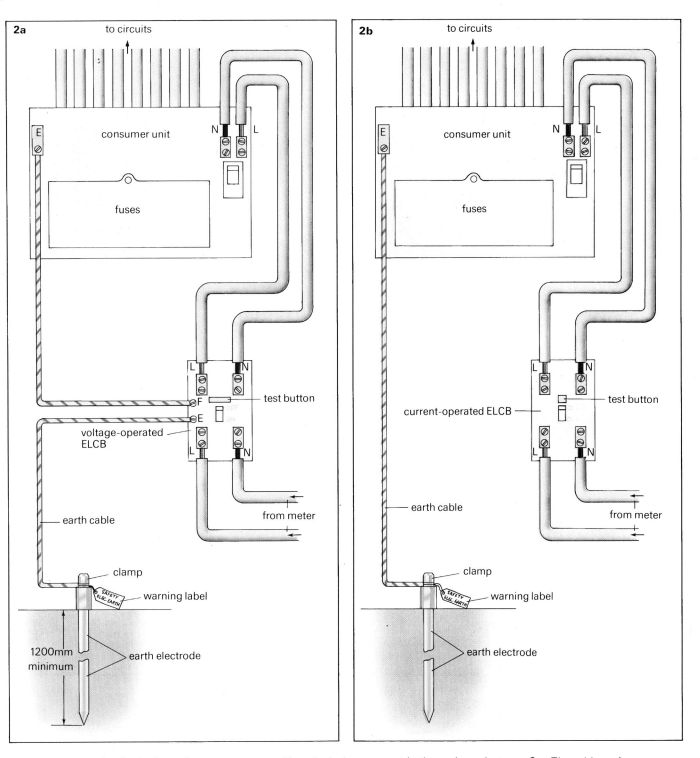

2a

to circuits

consumer unit

E

N   L

fuses

L   N

test button

F

E

voltage-operated
ELCB

L   N

earth cable

from meter

clamp

warning label

1200mm
minimum

earth electrode

2b

to circuits

consumer unit

E

N   L

fuses

current-operated ELCB

test button

L   N

earth cable

L   N

from meter

clamp

warning label

earth electrode

terminals. The mains leads from the meter are connected to one pair of live (L) and neutral (N) terminals; the other pair are load terminals which feed the installation and are normally connected by two leads to the mains terminals of the consumer unit. The subsidiary terminals are marked 'F' and 'E'. The F terminal is connected to the earth terminal on the consumer unit; the E terminal is connected to the earth clamp terminal of the earth electrode in the soil. Any leakage of current to the earth conductor in the main circuit passes through the tripping coil of the ELCB, energizing the electro-magnet which trips the circuit breaker. About 40 volts is needed to operate the tripping device and the current required to produce this voltage is very small.

Since the leakage current in the earth conductor must flow through the tripping coil to operate the release mechanism, this type of ELCB is not wholly reliable. For example, if fault current flows to earth via another path, such as a gas or water pipe (called a parallel earth path), it bypasses the ELCB and the ELCB does not trip. If this parallel earth path is satisfactory, sufficient current will flow to blow the fuse. If not, the gas or water pipework indoors will remain live and be dangerous.

Warning It is not a good idea to install two or more voltage-operated ELCBs to protect different sections of the installation, unless the respective earthing rods are at least 2.5m (or 8ft) apart and are 2.5m (or 8ft) away from buried water or gas pipes.

Current-operated This has been developed to over-

2a The wiring of a voltage-operated ELCB to the consumer unit and an earth electrode
2b The wiring of a current-operated ELCB to the consumer unit; the earth lead from the consumer unit goes directly to the earth electrode

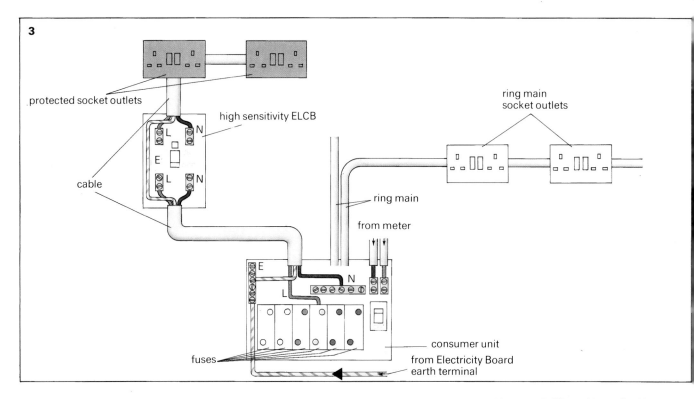

3

protected socket outlets

high sensitivity ELCB

cable

L   N

E

L   N

ring main
socket outlets

ring main

from meter

E

N

L

consumer unit

from Electricity Board
earth terminal

fuses

come the disadvantage of the voltage-operated ELCB. Although similar in style to the voltage type, its tripping coil is not energized directly by earth leakage current and has no earth conductors connected to it. There are four terminals – L and N mains terminals and L and N load terminals. The earthing lead from the consumer unit in this case goes direct to the earth electrode.

This type of ELCB works on the current balance principle – that current flowing into a circuit is equal to the current flowing out. For example, if 10amps flow into a circuit through the positive or live wire, you can expect 10amps to return via the negative or neutral wire. However, if a live wire touches earthed metal, some of the return current is diverted from the main circuit into the earth circuit; this causes an out-of-balance current in the main conductor. At the instant of the fault, the live pole of the mains switch will be carrying a lot of current and the neutral pole less, since some will be leaking to earth. By having an out-of-balance current sensing device and by connecting this to a tripping coil, you have a current-operated ELCB. No matter which path the earth leakage current takes, the sensing device will detect the out-of-balance in the mains lead and operate the tripping coil. The normal current-operated ELCB of 60–100-amps rating needs less than $\frac{1}{2}$-amp of out-of-balance current to operate, which means the earthing system needs to carry only that amount of current for the ELCB to work.

High sensitivity ELCB An ordinary ELCB gives no protection from direct electric shock, which is generally caused by touching a live wire or contact when also touching earthed metal or standing on the ground. With a normal current-operated circuit breaker this is because the amount of current required for it to operate is more than that required to electrocute someone; with a voltage-operated type it is because the current flowing to earth via another path (through the human body) does not flow through the ELCB trip coil. There is, however, a current-operated high sensitivity ELCB

which will protect you against electrocution if you touch a live wire while in contact with the ground either directly or via earthed metal.

It must be emphasized, however, that neither this ELCB nor any other device installed in the home will prevent you being electrocuted if you come into contact with both live and neutral poles of the 240V supply, even if you are standing on an insulated surface or wearing rubber boots in the garden. But if you are in contact with the ground at the same time, there is just a chance the high sensitivity ELCB will trip before you are electrocuted.

The high sensitivity ELCB, which trips at 30 milliamps in a fraction of a second, is especially useful for selective circuits such as those used for power tools, hedgecutters, mowers and other appliances where shock risk is fairly high. It should not be inserted in the main house circuits because, if condensation or some other small earth leakage current causes it to trip, it will cut off the power to the whole house. This is called nuisance tripping and is not only inconvenient, but it could also cause a serious accident.

A consumer unit is now available in which an ELCB protects some socket outlets and a conventional mains switch controls other circuits including lighting. Where a circuit is installed to supply a few socket outlets, it is best to use fittings of a different colour for the protected ones, so only these are used with high shock risk appliances.

A high sensitivity ELCB is available for plugging into a 13amp socket, from which you can run high risk power tools. Similar to an adaptor but larger, it is a useful safety device for the home.

It is also possible to fit a special socket outlet containing an ELCB in place of an existing double socket outlet, or as an addition to the circuit in the form of a spur.

The current Wiring Regulations require ELCB protection for any socket being used to power electrical equipment used out of doors; this can be provided by a special socket, as mentioned above, or by a separate ELCB protecting the circuit.

3 The wiring of a high sensitivity ELCB to the consumer unit, using 4.0 or 2.5sq mm cable, and to the socket outlets; use different coloured fittings to distinguish protected sockets from ring main sockets. There are now consumer units that incorporate an ELCB (current operated)

Wiring in an electric cooker

The average domestic electric cooker consists of an oven, a hob containing three or four rings and a grill. The conventional position for the grill is below the hob and usually built into it, although with some models it is positioned at eye level. Some models have a double oven.

The majority of cookers are compact, self-contained, free-standing units positioned against the wall and connected to a wall-mounted control switch by means of a trailing cable to allow the cooker to be moved forward when you want to clean behind it; a lockable bogie placed under the cooker will make it easier to move. Other models are built into the kitchen units; these usually have separate hob and oven sections and are termed split-level cookers, the oven being raised to a more practical height for cooking.

Circuit rating

Electric cookers are heavy current-consuming appliances, having loadings of up to 12kW (12,000 watts) for medium size cookers and even higher loadings for large, family size cookers including the double oven models. Cookers with loadings up to 12kW are usually supplied from circuits of 30amp current rating, while those in excess of 12kW are usually supplied from circuits of 45amp rating.

Although the maximum current demand of a 12kW cooker on a 240v supply is 50amps with everything switched on, allowance in rating the circuit has been made bearing in mind that rarely in the average home are all the rings, the grill and the oven in use at any one time. This means the circuit rating need only be 30amps. Even if everything is in use at one time, the current demand on the circuit at any one moment is still probably less than 50amps. This is because the rings, the grill and the oven are thermostatically controlled or include a simmering device which reduces the total current demand. In rating the circuit, allowance has also been made for an electric kettle plugged into the socket outlet of the cooker control unit and therefore taking current from the cooker circuit. Although a high-speed electric kettle takes up to 13amps from the circuit, kettles are assessed at only 5amps.

There is an official formula for arriving at the circuit requirements of an electric cooker, based on the average use when cooking for a family. The first 10amps is estimated at 100 percent and the remaining current at 30 percent; 5amps is allowed for an electric kettle plugged in the cooker control unit. If the current demand of a 12kW cooker is 50amps, the first 10amps is included, the remaining 40amps is estimated at 12amps and there is a 5amp allowance for a kettle. The total assessed load is 27amps and the circuit required is therefore 30amps.

Although the regulations permit a 12kW cooker to be supplied from a 30amp circuit, it is always worthwhile considering installing a 45amp circuit, provided the consumer unit will accept a 45amp fuse unit; some cannot. If there is no spare fuseway for an electric cooker circuit in the existing consumer unit and a separate switch fuse unit has to be installed, it is worth fitting one with a 45amp rating. A 45amp circuit means a larger size cable, but the extra cost is comparatively small and the work involved is the same as for a 30amp circuit.

Cooker circuit

A circuit for an electric cooker consists of a two core and earth flat PVC-sheathed cable starting at a fuseway and terminating at a 45amp cooker control unit or cooker switch. From the control unit or switch the same size cable runs through a cable entry into a terminal block in the cooker. Where the oven and hob are separate, one cooker control unit and switch can be used for both provided neither is more than 2m (6½ft) from it.

Top A free-standing electric cooker needs a 30 or 45amp circuit, depending on its loading; a microwave cooker, however, simply runs off a 13amp fused plug and socket outlet

Above A split level cooker requires the same circuit rating as an ordinary cooker

Cooker control unit This is a double pole switch and a switched 13amp socket outlet mounted on one panel. It is made with or without neon indicators and is available in either surface or flush-mounted versions.

Cooker switch This is simply a 45amp double pole plate switch without a kettle socket outlet, with or without a neon indicator and available in surface or flush-mounted versions. The cooker switch is cheaper than a control unit since it has no socket outlet; it can be fitted when you do not want to operate the kettle from the control unit, which can often be a disadvantage and also potentially dangerous. If the control unit is fixed in the traditional position above the cooker, the kettle flex could trail over the rings; if these are switched on, the flex will burn and could start a fire or give an electric shock before the fuse blows.

With the introduction of the ring circuit, the traditional single utility plug and socket in the kitchen has largely been replaced by numerous socket outlets; this means a socket on the control unit is unnecessary, since the kettle can be used from one of these extra socket outlets.

Cable sizes

For a 30amp cooker circuit, you should use 6sq mm cable and 10sq mm cable for a 45amp circuit. Cable is available in grey or white sheathing; white is usually preferred, especially if part of the cable is fixed to the surface and if the trailing section between the control unit or switch and the cooker is visible.

Cable route

Having decided on the position for the control unit or switch, which must be within 2m (or 6ft) of the cooker so it can quickly be reached by someone using the cooker, choose the route for the cable. Where the consumer unit is on the same floor as the control unit in the kitchen (as in the conventional house), the simplest route is under the ground floor – assuming this is of timber construction. Run a cable down the wall below the consumer unit and pass it behind the skirting (if any) and into the void of the suspended floor. Feed it under the joists, where it can lay unfixed on the sub-floor, and up through a hole drilled in the flooring immediately below the position of the control unit or switch.

If you have a solid ground floor (as in many modern houses), you will have to find an alternative route. This usually means running the cable up the wall above the consumer unit and into the void above the ceiling, under the upstairs floorboards and down through a hole in the ceiling above the control unit or switch. If you adopt this route, you will have to lift floorboards and probably drill through joists.

Where the bathroom – and particularly a combined bathroom/WC – is above the kitchen, you may have problems raising floorboards and the

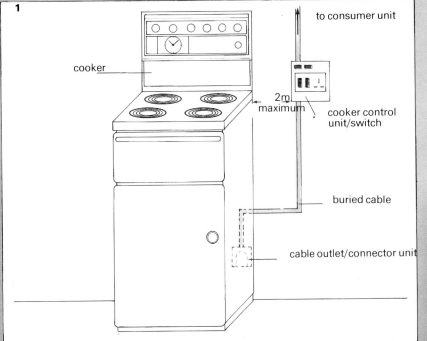

to consumer unit

cooker

2m maximum

cooker control unit/switch

buried cable

cable outlet/connector unit

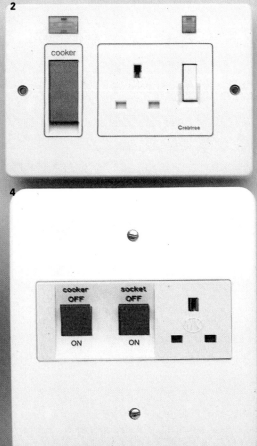

1 The wiring layout for a free-standing cooker. The cable outlet or connector unit is hidden when the cooker is in position against the wall; make sure there is sufficient cable between the cable outlet or connector unit and the cooker to allow the cooker to be pulled forward
2 & 3 Cooker control units (45amp double pole switch and 13amp switched socket outlet) with neon indicators
4 Cooker control unit

cooker

cooker OFF   socket OFF
ON   ON

cooker OFF   socket OFF
ON   ON

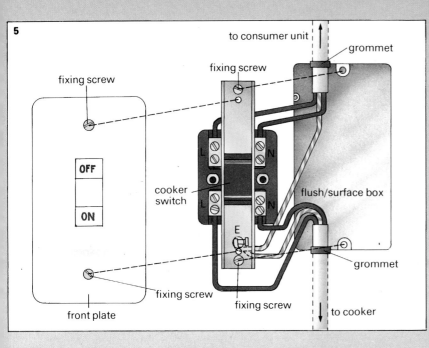

5 Wiring a cooker switch; with the type shown you must remove the front plate from the switch before connecting the cables

6 Cooker control unit

7 45amp double pole cooker switch

8 Cooker control unit (30/50amp)

9 Connector unit

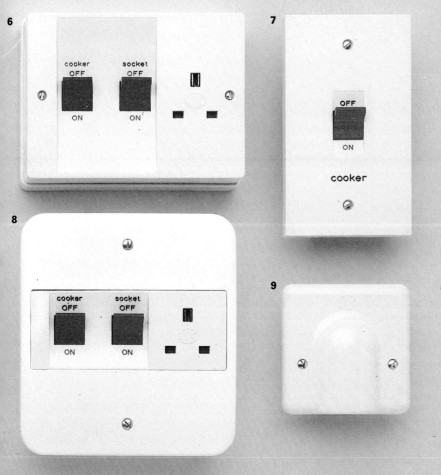

Fitting control unit

Surface-mounted control units are available in two versions. One is all-plastic, with an enclosed back and thin plastic sections which are knocked out to provide entry holes for the cable; it is fixed to the wall with a couple of screws. The second type consists of a square plate, usually metal, which is mounted on a metal box; both are finished in white and the box is fixed to the wall with screws. The box has a selection of knock-out holes fitted with blanks, two of which are knocked out for the cables and fitted with PVC grommets to protect the cable sheathing. A range of smaller, oblong plastic control units is also available; these are mounted on plastic surface boxes or metal flush boxes.

The standard flush-mounted control unit is also of square plate design, mounted on a matching metal box sunk into the wall so it sits flush with the plaster. This box also has knock-out holes for the cable and these must be fitted with PVC grommets. This type is suitable where the cable is buried in the wall; where it is not possible to bury all the cable – such as with a tiled wall – you will have to cut short channels above and below the box to feed in the cable.

A cable trailing down a wall from the control unit to the cooker is not only unsightly, but can also be an obstruction. It can be fixed to the wall with cable clips for most of its length provided the final loop is left free in case you want to pull out the cooker from the wall. However undue strain is likely to occur on the bottom clip and to overcome this you can fit a connector unit.

Connector unit This consists of a terminal block fitted into a metal flush box and a moulded plastic cover plate with an entry hole for the cable. The connector unit is fitted about 1200mm (or 2½ft) above the floor – or lower if necessary; the cable running down from the control unit is connected to the terminals, the cable preferably being buried in the wall. The trailing length of cable running from the cooker is also connected to the terminals on the connector unit and the sheathing is clamped to prevent any strain being exerted on the terminals when the cooker is moved out from the wall. If the cooker is changed or temporarily removed, you can disconnect it easily by releasing the cooker cable from these terminals.

Cable outlet unit An alternative arrangement is a cable outlet unit. Here the cable between the control unit and the cooker is not cut, but merely passes through, and is clamped in, the outlet box, which should be positioned behind the cooker.

Connecting control unit

Having fixed the box to the wall with about 200mm (or 8in) of each cable within the box, strip the sheathing off the end of each cable, leaving about 25mm (1in) within the box; strip about 8mm (⅜in) of insulation from the ends of the four current carrying conductors. Slip green/yellow PVC sleeving over the bare earth wires, leaving about 8mm (⅜in) exposed. Connect the red circuit conductor to the mains terminal marked L and the black to the mains terminal marked N. Connect the red conductor of the cooker cable to the load terminal marked L and the black to the load terminal marked N. Connect the two earth conductors to the earth terminal of the control unit. Arrange the wires neatly in the box, fix the switch to the box and screw the cover and

cable route will have to be diverted. Under these conditions it is best to prepare the route before buying the cable, so you can measure 'the exact length required and save buying too much of this relatively expensive material.

For a single-storey building with a solid floor, the cable can readily be run in the roof space. In a flat which has solid floors and where there is no access to the ceiling above, surface wiring will be necessary. Here the cable can be enclosed in conduits which can be in the form of hollow skirting.

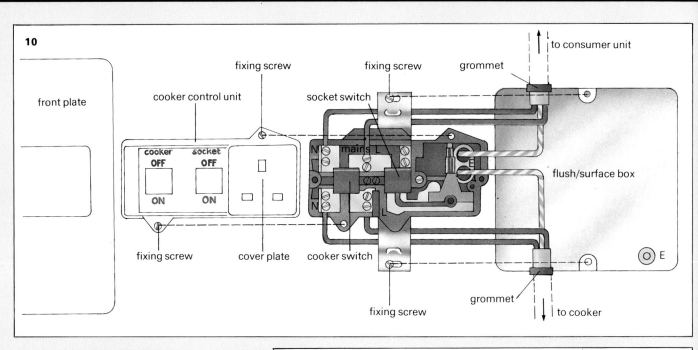

10

front plate

cooker control unit

fixing screw

fixing screw

socket switch

grommet

to consumer unit

cooker OFF ON
socket OFF ON

mains

N L

E

N L

flush/surface box

fixing screw

cover plate

cooker switch

fixing screw

grommet

E

fixing screw

to cooker

front plates to the switch assembly. Separate cables are not required for the socket outlet since this is connected internally to the cooker terminals.

The method of connection is the same for a cooker switch. With a unit made entirely of plastic, the cables are threaded into the unit with the cover removed and the unit fixed to the wall. The cable connections are then made and the cover replaced.

Connecting to consumer unit

With the mains switched to OFF, remove the consumer unit cover, run the cable into the unit and prepare the end of the conductors as before. The red wire is connected to the fuseway terminal, the black to the neutral terminal bank and the green/yellow PVC-sleeved earth wire to the earth terminal bank. Insert and fix the fuse unit, replace the cover and put the main switch back to ON.

Switch fuse unit Where there is no spare fuseway, you will have to install a separate switch fuse unit consisting of a double pole 60amp mains switch and a fuse unit of 30 or 45amp current rating. Fit the unit near the consumer unit and connect two 3m (or 10ft) lengths of 10sq mm PVC-sheathed cable – a red insulation cable to the L terminal and a black insulation cable to the N terminal. Also connect 6sq mm green/yellow insulated earth cable to the E terminal. The cooker circuit cable is wired to load or circuit terminals as for the consumer unit.

The mains leads are connected to the mains by the Electricity Board. You may also have to fit a two-way service connector box for the two pairs of meter leads you will now have.

Connecting split-level cooker

The same circuit cable from the 30 or 45amp fuseway to the cooker control unit or switch is required for a split-level cooker; the one control will serve both sections provided each is within 2m (or 6ft) of the control unit. If the control unit is fixed midway between the two units, they can be spaced up to 4m (or 12ft) apart, which is adequate for most kitchen layouts. Otherwise a second control unit is required, one being linked to the other using the same size

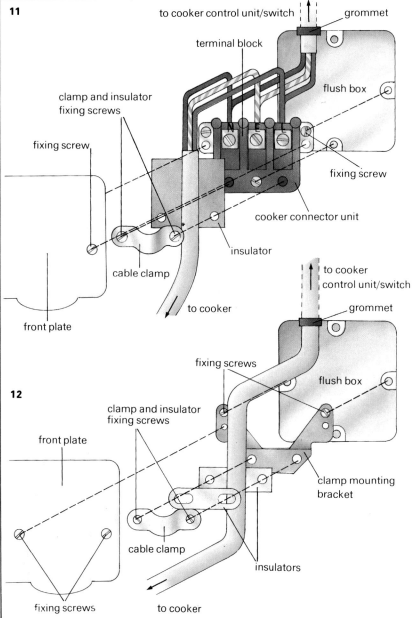

11

to cooker control unit/switch

grommet

terminal block

clamp and insulator fixing screws

fixing screw

flush box

N E L

fixing screw

cooker connector unit

cable clamp

insulator

to cooker

front plate

to cooker control unit/switch

grommet

fixing screws

flush box

12

clamp and insulator fixing screws

front plate

clamp mounting bracket

cable clamp

insulators

fixing screws

to cooker

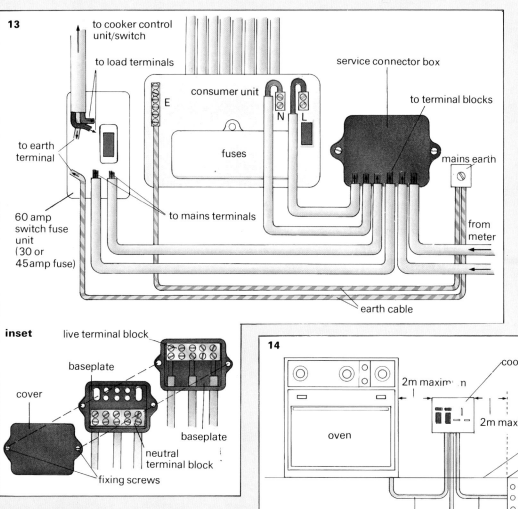

13

to cooker control unit/switch

to load terminals

consumer unit

E

N L

fuses

service connector box

to terminal blocks

to earth terminal

mains earth

60 amp switch fuse unit (30 or 45 amp fuse)

to mains terminals

from meter

earth cable

inset

live terminal block

baseplate

cover

baseplate

neutral terminal block

fixing screws

10 Wiring a control unit; remove the front and cover plates before connecting the cables. 11 Wiring a connector unit; use a box with four mounting lugs. 12 Connecting a cable outlet unit. 13 Connecting to the mains if there is no spare fuseway in the consumer unit; the wiring at the service connector box (**inset**) 14 The wiring for a split level cooker supplied from one control unit or switch between the two sections. 15 The wiring for a split level cooker supplied from one control unit or switch at one side of the two sections. 16 The wiring for a split level cooker supplied from two control units or switches looped together by the circuit cable

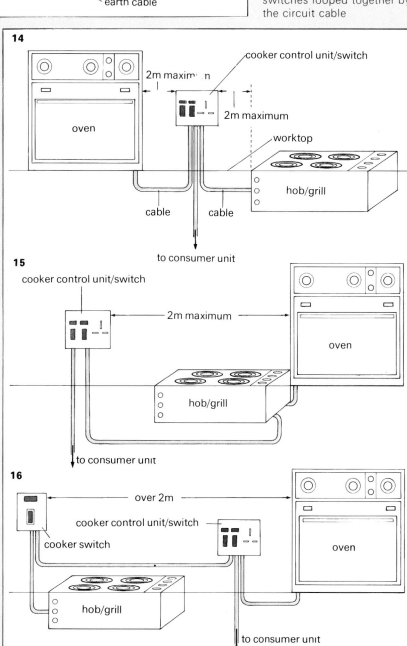

14

cooker control unit/switch

2m maximum

2m maximum

oven

worktop

hob/grill

cable

cable

to consumer unit

15

cooker control unit/switch

2m maximum

oven

hob/grill

to consumer unit

16

over 2m

cooker control unit/switch

cooker switch

oven

hob/grill

to consumer unit

cable as for the circuit.

Where, as in most cases, the one control unit is to serve both sections of a split-level cooker, you can either run two cables from the load side of the control unit – one to each section – or, depending on the relative positions, you can run one cable to the nearer of the two sections and then run a cable from the terminals of the nearer one to the other section.

Every cable must be of the same size as the main circuit cable, even though one or both may carry less than the total current. The reason for this is that, with no intervening fuse, the cable rating is determined by the rating of the circuit fuse.

The cables being run direct to the sections of a split-level cooker can be fixed to the surface or buried in the wall to suit individual requirements.

Connecting small cookers

Microwave cookers, which are becoming increasingly popular in the home, have loadings around 500 watts and are fitted with flex to be run off a 13 amp fused plug and socket outlet. These, therefore, need no special circuit. The same applies to baby cookers, which have a maximum loading of 3 kW.

51

Immersion heaters

One great advantage of an immersion heater fitted to your hot water cylinder is that it can be used to supply as much or as little hot water around the home as you need at any particular time. It can also supplement other heating systems such as gas, oil or solid fuel. With care, you can fit it yourself.

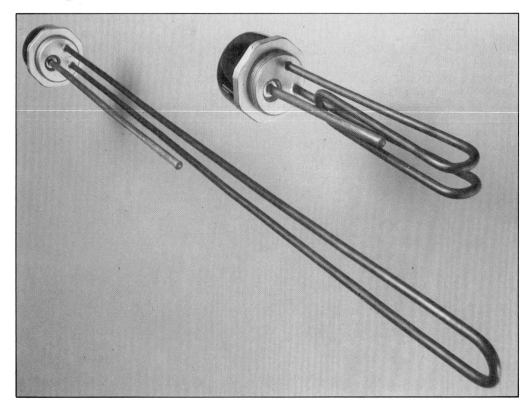

Left Immersion heaters are available in different lengths. You can buy a dual-element model, which heats either the top or all of the cylinder, or a single element one. If you decide on the single heater, you will find it is more economical to fit two, one at the top of the cylinder and the other lower down near the bottom
1 Types of immersion heater shown fitted into the hot water cylinder
1a Single element in varying lengths to suit different size cylinders
1b Separate heaters can be fitted so the top of the cylinder is heated for small amounts of water and all the cylinder heated when larger amounts are needed
1c The dual-element heater does the same job, but has the advantage of being a single fitting

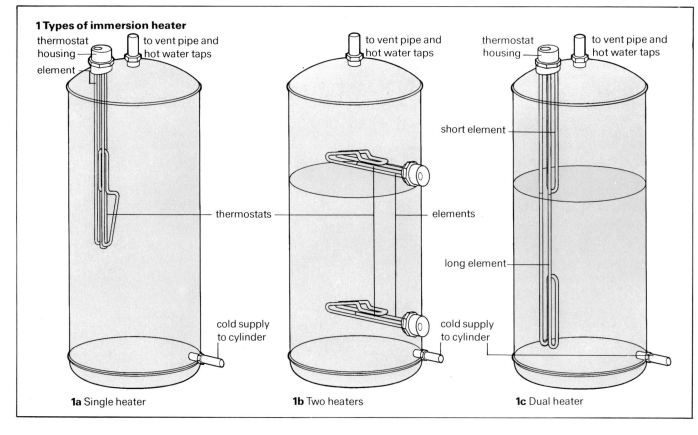

1 Types of immersion heater

thermostat housing — element — to vent pipe and hot water taps

to vent pipe and hot water taps

thermostat housing — to vent pipe and hot water taps

short element

thermostats — elements

long element

cold supply to cylinder

cold supply to cylinder

1a Single heater **1b** Two heaters **1c** Dual heater

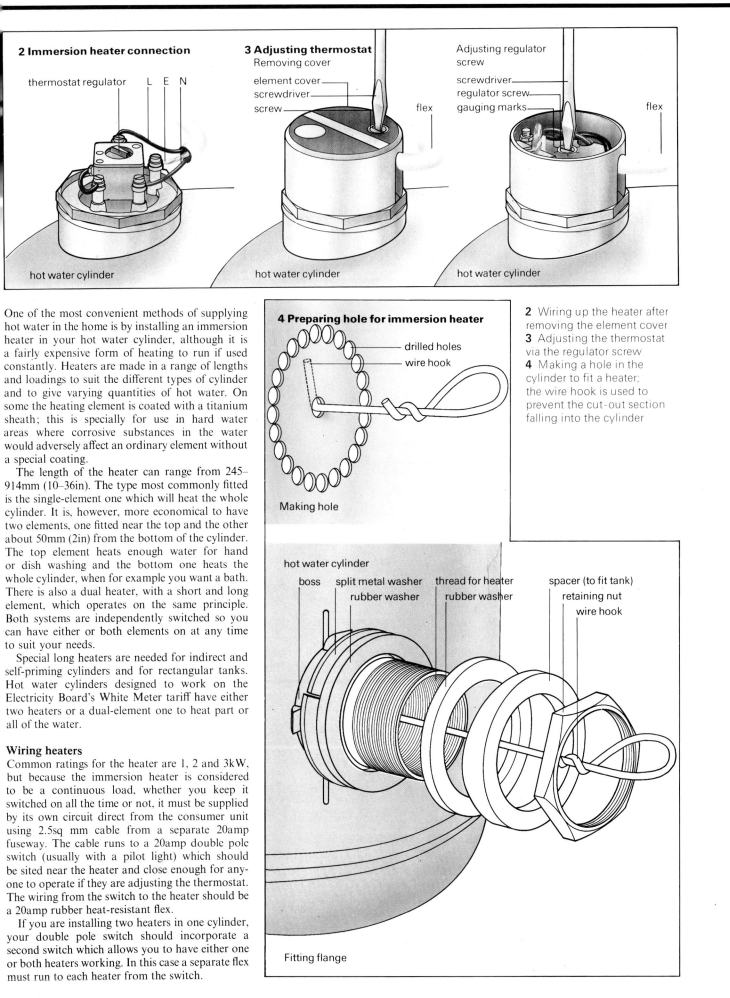

2 Immersion heater connection

thermostat regulator   L E N

hot water cylinder

3 Adjusting thermostat
Removing cover

element cover
screwdriver
screw

flex

hot water cylinder

Adjusting regulator
screw

screwdriver
regulator screw
gauging marks

flex

hot water cylinder

One of the most convenient methods of supplying hot water in the home is by installing an immersion heater in your hot water cylinder, although it is a fairly expensive form of heating to run if used constantly. Heaters are made in a range of lengths and loadings to suit the different types of cylinder and to give varying quantities of hot water. On some the heating element is coated with a titanium sheath; this is specially for use in hard water areas where corrosive substances in the water would adversely affect an ordinary element without a special coating.

The length of the heater can range from 245–914mm (10–36in). The type most commonly fitted is the single-element one which will heat the whole cylinder. It is, however, more economical to have two elements, one fitted near the top and the other about 50mm (2in) from the bottom of the cylinder. The top element heats enough water for hand or dish washing and the bottom one heats the whole cylinder, when for example you want a bath. There is also a dual heater, with a short and long element, which operates on the same principle. Both systems are independently switched so you can have either or both elements on at any time to suit your needs.

Special long heaters are needed for indirect and self-priming cylinders and for rectangular tanks. Hot water cylinders designed to work on the Electricity Board's White Meter tariff have either two heaters or a dual-element one to heat part or all of the water.

Wiring heaters
Common ratings for the heater are 1, 2 and 3kW, but because the immersion heater is considered to be a continuous load, whether you keep it switched on all the time or not, it must be supplied by its own circuit direct from the consumer unit using 2.5sq mm cable from a separate 20amp fuseway. The cable runs to a 20amp double pole switch (usually with a pilot light) which should be sited near the heater and close enough for anyone to operate if they are adjusting the thermostat. The wiring from the switch to the heater should be a 20amp rubber heat-resistant flex.

If you are installing two heaters in one cylinder, your double pole switch should incorporate a second switch which allows you to have either one or both heaters working. In this case a separate flex must run to each heater from the switch.

4 Preparing hole for immersion heater

drilled holes
wire hook

Making hole

2 Wiring up the heater after removing the element cover
3 Adjusting the thermostat via the regulator screw
4 Making a hole in the cylinder to fit a heater; the wire hook is used to prevent the cut-out section falling into the cylinder

hot water cylinder

boss   split metal washer   thread for heater   spacer (to fit tank)
    rubber washer   rubber washer   retaining nut
    wire hook

Fitting flange

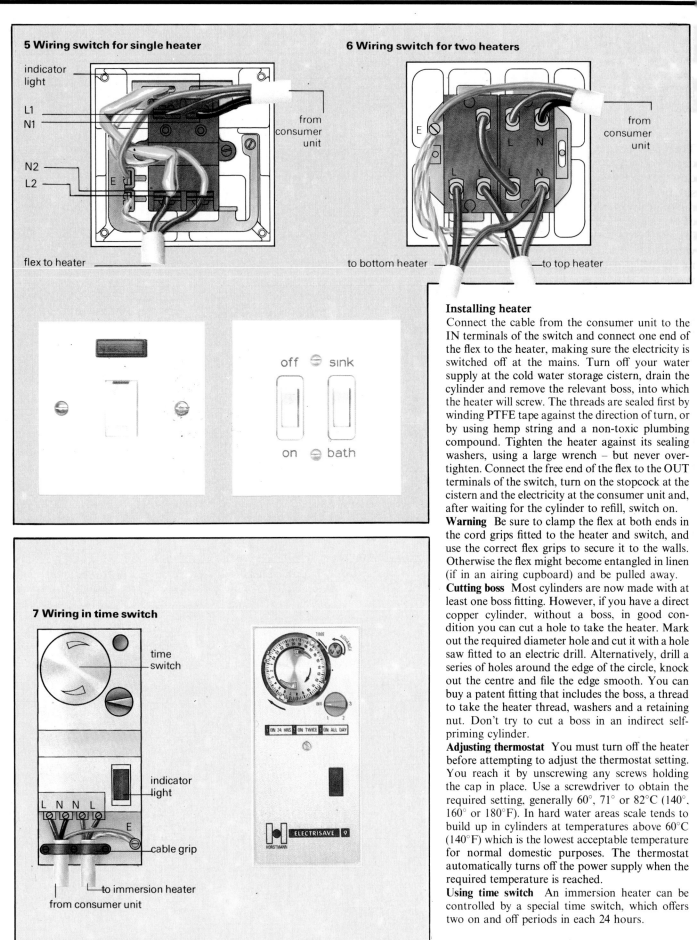

5 Wiring switch for single heater

indicator light

L1
N1

N2
L2

from consumer unit

flex to heater

6 Wiring switch for two heaters

E
L
N

from consumer unit

to bottom heater ——— to top heater

off ⊖ sink

on ⊖ bath

7 Wiring in time switch

time switch

indicator light

L N N L

E

cable grip

to immersion heater

from consumer unit

ELECTRISAVE 9
HORSTMANN

Installing heater

Connect the cable from the consumer unit to the IN terminals of the switch and connect one end of the flex to the heater, making sure the electricity is switched off at the mains. Turn off your water supply at the cold water storage cistern, drain the cylinder and remove the relevant boss, into which the heater will screw. The threads are sealed first by winding PTFE tape against the direction of turn, or by using hemp string and a non-toxic plumbing compound. Tighten the heater against its sealing washers, using a large wrench – but never over-tighten. Connect the free end of the flex to the OUT terminals of the switch, turn on the stopcock at the cistern and the electricity at the consumer unit and, after waiting for the cylinder to refill, switch on.

Warning Be sure to clamp the flex at both ends in the cord grips fitted to the heater and switch, and use the correct flex grips to secure it to the walls. Otherwise the flex might become entangled in linen (if in an airing cupboard) and be pulled away.

Cutting boss Most cylinders are now made with at least one boss fitting. However, if you have a direct copper cylinder, without a boss, in good condition you can cut a hole to take the heater. Mark out the required diameter hole and cut it with a hole saw fitted to an electric drill. Alternatively, drill a series of holes around the edge of the circle, knock out the centre and file the edge smooth. You can buy a patent fitting that includes the boss, a thread to take the heater thread, washers and a retaining nut. Don't try to cut a boss in an indirect self-priming cylinder.

Adjusting thermostat You must turn off the heater before attempting to adjust the thermostat setting. You reach it by unscrewing any screws holding the cap in place. Use a screwdriver to obtain the required setting, generally 60°, 71° or 82°C (140°, 160° or 180°F). In hard water areas scale tends to build up in cylinders at temperatures above 60°C (140°F) which is the lowest acceptable temperature for normal domestic purposes. The thermostat automatically turns off the power supply when the required temperature is reached.

Using time switch An immersion heater can be controlled by a special time switch, which offers two on and off periods in each 24 hours.

5 Wiring up switch when fitting single heater
6 Wiring up switch when fitting two heaters
7 Wiring up time switch to heater

Bathroom fittings

The bathroom can be one of the most dangerous places in the home if you don't follow the rules for electrical safety. But it can also be one of the most comfortable with the introduction of electrical fittings. As long as you install them correctly they will not only work at maximum efficiency, but need never be a cause for anxiety to you or your family.

There is nothing worse than a bleak, chilly bathroom to greet you on a cold morning. Yet even the largest bathroom can be greatly improved with the addition of a wall-mounted infra-red heater for instant warmth, a small oil-fitted electric radiator, a heated towel rail (to warm towels when you have a bath and to dry them afterwards), a combined heater/light unit or a shaver socket combined with a mirror light.

Two important factors, however, must be remembered: these installations must be correctly wired and appliances must be fixed so securely that they can be removed only by using proper tools. Correct wiring means no socket outlets – except for the shaver – are permitted inside a bathroom (or washroom) and only cord-operated switches are allowed inside the room if they are within reach of the bath or shower; this is taken to be a distance of 2m (6ft 6in).

Heated towel rail

A good selection of these is available, so choose the largest one that will fit in your bathroom. It is a good idea to buy one that incorporates a pilot light because this means you are less likely to forget to turn it off. Towel rails must be connected to the ring circuit through a switched fused connection unit that is sited outside the bathroom.

Decide where you are going to install the appliance, first making sure the plaster or plasterboard wall is strong enough to make a secure fixing. Use a spirit level to check the appliance is being fixed horizontally and mark with a pencil the fixing holes for the screws. Drill and plug the holes.

Prepare the route for your cable (2.5sq mm twin core and earth PVC-sheathed) from the ring circuit to the switched fuse connection unit; install the unit as close to the appliance as possible – but outside the bathroom. Decide on the route for the appliance flex to reach the connection unit. If this entails a long run you may have to install a flexible cord outlet box – linked to the connection unit with 2.5sq mm twin core and earth cable. The wires from the appliance are then connected to their corresponding terminals on the cord outlet box.

When you have completed the installation, check all terminal and fixing screws, turn on the mains and switch on the appliance to check it is working.
Oil-filled radiator The installation method for oil-filled radiators is similar to that for fitting a heated towel rail.

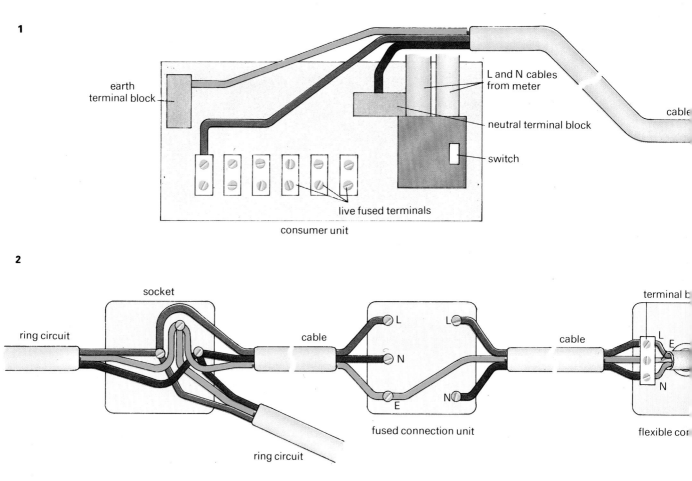

1

earth
terminal block

L and N cables
from meter

neutral terminal block

switch

cable

live fused terminals

consumer unit

2

socket

ring circuit

cable

L

L

N

cable

terminal b

L

E

E

N

N

N

fused connection unit

flexible co

ring circuit

Wall heater

This must also be fed from the ring circuit, using a switched fused connection unit and a flexible cord outlet as described for a towel rail. The heater should be fixed as high on the wall as possible and preferably not above a bath or a shower. Alternatively you may connect the appliance to a cord-operated isolating switch (incorporating a pilot light) and connect the switch to the ring circuit via a connection unit as before.

The appliance is fixed to the wall with plugs and screws; always ensure it is properly secured before connecting up and switching on.

Light/heater units

The ultimate in space-saving, this unit incorporates a lamp in the centre of a ceiling fitting with a heating element around the outside. A cord-operated switch within the unit operates the heater. The master switch should be a cord-operated ceiling switch. It should not be connected to a lighting circuit because many units have a total loading of 850 watts and if used simultaneously with a number of other lights on the circuit it could overload the maximum 1200 watts capacity and cause a fuse to blow in the consumer unit – not a happy thought if you are in the bath at the time.

There are two ways of supplying such a unit. One is through a switched fused connection unit, the other by running a separate circuit from a spare fuseway in the consumer unit, using either 1 or 1.5sq mm twin core and earth cable. You must take great care in connecting up at the consumer unit; the circuit should be controlled by a 5amp fuse.

The appliance should be securely mounted to a timber batten screwed between joists in the ceiling

3

ring circuit

L

N

E

cable

L

N

E

junction box

ring circuit

fused conne

4

from fused connection
unit or direct from
consumer unit

E L L

N N

pull switch

1 Wiring appliance direct to consumer unit. **2** Wiring appliance to ring circuit socket outlet via fused connection unit. **3** Wiring appliance to junction box via fused connection unit. **4** Wiring appliance to fused connection unit or consumer unit and including pull switch. **5** Wiring shaver socket to ceiling rose.

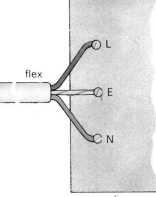

appliance

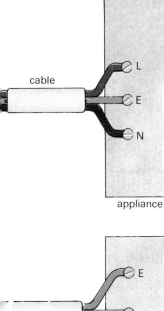

flex

appliance

cable

appliance

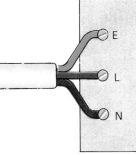

appliance

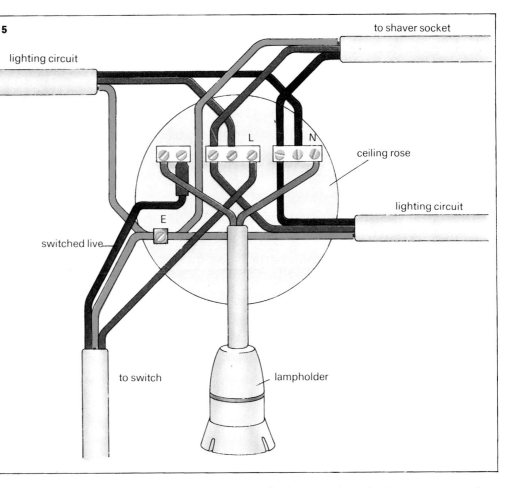

lighting circuit

to shaver socket

ceiling rose

lighting circuit

L

N

E

switched live

to switch

lampholder

or roof space. Connect the ceiling cord-operated switch between the appliance and the connection unit; if you are running the appliance from the consumer unit, fit an isolating ceiling cord-operated switch within reach of the appliance.

Ceiling rose If by installing a heat/light unit you are making the existing ceiling rose redundant, you must remove the pendant flex, rose, switch wires and switch. Having disconnected the switch wire at the rose, disconnect at the switch or switches; pull the cable through from the ceiling space and discard it, replastering any recess where the switch was fixed.

You must install a junction box between the joists above the rose and use this to seal off (or terminate) the cables that run to the rose. You will have to take great care doing this, ensuring the conductors fitted to the rose are connected to their corresponding terminals in the junction box. With an older installation, earthing was probably not used; if earthing is used, connect the earth to its proper terminal in the box. With an older installation you may have difficulty identifying all the cables. If you have any doubts, always seek expert advice – don't trust your own judgement.

Shaver sockets

The specially designed shaver socket for use in the bathroom is available in several types: some come complete with a mirror light. The shaver supply unit can be connected directly to the lighting circuit without using a fuse in the spur, because it contains an isolating transformer. The unit has a two-pin socket that accepts British, Continental and American standard round and flat-pin plugs. It is possible to buy a dual voltage socket outlet for 240 or 115

volts in cases where the shaver does not adapt. Shaver sockets are also made without isolating transformers for use in other rooms.

It is impossible to run other appliances off a shaver socket because a thermal unit will cause them to cut out.

Remember when installing a shaver socket that anyone who is short-sighted needs to get quite close to a mirror with their spectacles off. So avoid placing it over a deep sink or cupboard that forces them to stand and peer. If you have a rechargeable electric razor, make sure there is a shelf near the socket where you can leave the shaver to recharge.

Mirror light This is a boon when you are making-up, or shaving with an electric or wet razor. Units are available which combine a striplight and a shaver socket at the end.

Having decided the position of the shaver and/or mirror light unit, trace a pencil outline round the box (available flush, semi-flush or surface-mounted) or mark the securing screw holes. Thread your cable through a hole drilled in the wall through the back of your surface-mounted box or through knock-out holes. Secure the box. Trim the cable sheath, strip the insulation material and connect up in the normal way to the correct terminals. The earth terminal is generally riveted in the base of the box; the live and neutral conductors go to terminals on the reverse side of the socket unit. Then secure the unit to the box with the screws provided, turn on the mains and test the light.

Warning If you have any doubts about the safety or suitability of a product, don't buy it. The yellow and blue label of the British Electrotechnical Approvals Board attached to a product proves it has been tested to the British Standard for electrical safety.

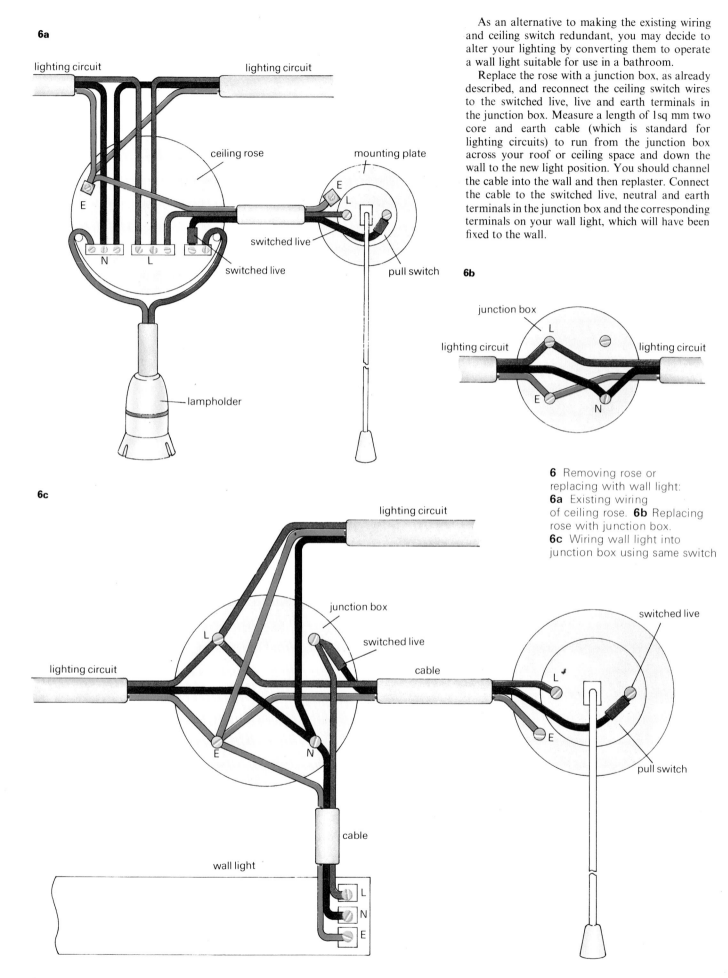

6a

lighting circuit

lighting circuit

ceiling rose

mounting plate

E

L

E

L

N

L

switched live

switched live

pull switch

lampholder

As an alternative to making the existing wiring and ceiling switch redundant, you may decide to alter your lighting by converting them to operate a wall light suitable for use in a bathroom.

Replace the rose with a junction box, as already described, and reconnect the ceiling switch wires to the switched live, live and earth terminals in the junction box. Measure a length of 1sq mm two core and earth cable (which is standard for lighting circuits) to run from the junction box across your roof or ceiling space and down the wall to the new light position. You should channel the cable into the wall and then replaster. Connect the cable to the switched live, neutral and earth terminals in the junction box and the corresponding terminals on your wall light, which will have been fixed to the wall.

6b

junction box

L

lighting circuit

lighting circuit

E

N

6 Removing rose or replacing with wall light: **6a** Existing wiring of ceiling rose. **6b** Replacing rose with junction box. **6c** Wiring wall light into junction box using same switch

6c

lighting circuit

junction box

switched live

L

cable

switched live

lighting circuit

L

lighting circuit

E

N

E

cable

pull switch

wall light

L

N

E

Outside wiring

Wiring to sockets or lighting points attached to the outside walls of a house can be part of the domestic circuit. Wiring to a point in the garden, greenhouse or separate garage, however, has to be treated as a different installation, with its own main switch and fuse unit. Sockets supplying outdoor appliances must now have ELCB protection (see page 282).

Because wind and rough weather will cause wear and tear, sockets, switches and cables must be tough, weatherproof and protected from the possibility of accidental damage. Professional help with outside wiring is essential because electricity used outside is potentially more dangerous than inside.

Surface wiring
Wiring a porch light, socket or switch onto the outside wall of a house is not difficult as long as you use weatherproof equipment. Sockets are usually in galvanized steel with covers and the switches are plastic. It is best to keep wiring on an outside wall to a minimum; it should be protected in plastic tubing or conduit and the connections, where the cable joins the switch or socket or light fitting, have to be water- and weatherproof. The wiring can be taken as a spur from the ring main, although a porch or outside light can be taken from a lighting point, as described earlier in the book; in this case the cable goes through the wall as close to the light as possible. Study the wiring layout of the house to plan the shortest route from the new position to the existing wiring; this will give a neater installation.

To take a cable from the inside of a house to the outside, drill a hole through the wall using a masonry bit of up to 300mm (1ft) long if it is a cavity wall. Insert a short length of plastic tube or conduit; this must be angled so the outside end is lower than the inside (to keep out rainwater) and cemented in place. Fit an elbow to the outside end.

Overhead wiring
With the overhead method of wiring, the PVC twin core and earth cable is supported by a galvanized steel cable called a catenary wire. The power cable

is relieved of any stress or strain by being clipped and taped to the catenary wire which is itself suspended from permanent supports not less than 3.5m (11ft 6in) above ground or 5.2m (17ft) if above a drive. To get the right height you may have to attach a weather-treated post to the greenhouse or garage and brace it to withstand strong winds. You must fit supporting vine eyes, one into a heavy duty plug on the house wall and the other into the side of the post near the top. The ends of the catenary wire are threaded through the eyes and twisted firmly round the main length of wire.

Since the catenary wire will be under strain for many years, it is vital to have a strong joint at each end. It is also a good idea to have an adjustable eye bolt fitting or a turnbuckle at one end of the catenary wire so it can be stretched tight. The catenary wire must be earthed using single core 6sq mm PVC-insulated earth wire connected to it by a corrosion-resistant screw-type connector and connected to the mains earth point in the house. Cable from the switch fuse should come through the wall using a tube or conduit as already described. The mains cable should be 2.5sq mm or 4sq mm and in one continuous length from the switch fuse to the new switch or socket.

A downward rainwater 'drip loop' of slack is usually left at each end and the supply cable is attached to the catenary wire by using slings or bitumen-impregnated insulating tape; this is turned two or three times between the cable and wire. Non-corrosive buckle-type cable clips are wrapped round the tape for strength.

Underground wiring
You can run ordinary PVC-sheathed cable underground so long as it is protected by impact-resistant PVC conduit. However, except for very long runs it is probably simpler to use special cable, armoured PVC-insulated cable being recommended. It has two cores – red and black insulated – and an extruded covering of black PVC over the galvanized wire armour; the wire armour usually serves as the

1 Outdoor plug, socket and cover
2 Components of outdoor gland used for connecting armoured cable to metal box
3 Twin core armoured cable, stripped back to show various layers, connected to metal box with indoor gland; separate earth wire connects to earth terminal on metal box
4 Exploded indoor gland
5 Weatherproofed switch
6 Twin core armoured cable connected to metal box with outdoor gland
7 Three core armoured cable stripped back to show various layers; yellow core is used as earth wire

earth conductor. It is necessary to fit a metal screwed compression gland, secured by a lock nut and bush, over the wire armour at each end of the cable; this gland fits the conduit entry hole of a flush metal box, fixed inside the building or house, which is used as a junction box if the entry point of the armoured cable is some distance from the main switch or switch fuse. A terminal block inside the box is used to connect the armoured cable to ordinary twin core and earth PVC-sheathed cable. Alternatively the cable can be run to the switch mounting box. In both cases a short length of 4.0sq mm single core green/yellow PVC-insulated cable is used to connect the switch or terminal block earth terminal to the earth terminal on the box.

Some Electricity Boards may insist on the use of three core armoured cable, the yellow core being used for the earth and enclosed in green/yellow sleeving for identification.

A more expensive cable is the mineral-insulated, copper-clad type (MICC); this has two wires inside a protective copper tube which also serves as an earth connection. With mineral-insulated cable it is necessary to fit a seal at each end; if the cable runs directly into the switch and fuse unit, choose a seal which has an earth wire termination. A screwed gland can also be fitted with each seal if required. The cable runs from the main switch and fuse unit in the house to the control panel in the building outside, taking as direct a route as possible but avoiding all places likely to be disturbed in the future. The trench must be dug about 500mm (20in) deep and care taken not to damage any water or drainpipes and other cables you encounter. If there is a space below the ground floor of your house, it is easy to have a hole knocked through the wall; but be careful not to interfere with the damp proof course. The cable needs to be protected at points where it is exposed and securely fixed to the wall using special clips designed for the purpose. Additional protection can be given by galvanized steel channelling screwed to the brick or woodwork.

Below Layout showing wiring from house to outbuildings — over or underground — with details of connections to consumer unit inside house (**inset A**), taking cable through wall inside conduit pipe and connecting to catenary wire (**inset B**), fixing catenary wire to post (**inset C**) and outbuilding control panel (**inset D**); when wiring up use cable for lights and flex for other appliances

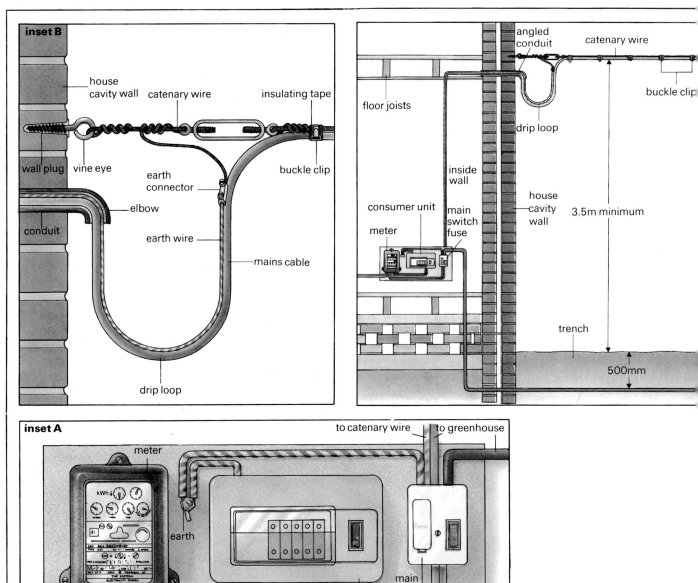

Control panels

In an integral or attached garage the cable can run direct to sockets and light fittings; but ideally the cable should terminate in a control panel with a main switch. In the damper atmosphere of a greenhouse or garden shed, a control panel is strongly advisable for safety; switched points and socket outlets can then be connected to the switch. Permanent switches and fused connection units with red neon indicators are preferable, since most of the equipment will be permanently connected. With a plug and socket there is always a risk of damp working its way between the face of the plug and the socket surface, resulting in a current leakage. Providing ELCB protection for all socket outlets on the panel is required by the Wiring Regulations.

Fused connection units, switches and sockets should be installed 1200mm (4ft) from the floor and wired with twin core and earth PVC-sheathed 2.5sq mm cable. The cable is taken from each in turn back to the outlet on the main switch. Fused connection units and sockets should be mounted on metal mounting boxes inset into a timber board, or on moulded plastic surface-mounted boxes, with cable holes drilled through the board.

In a greenhouse fit a strong frame to the back of the board to protect the cable and leave access for the mains cable. Once the wiring is complete, fit a back cover of weatherproof plywood and mount the board at chest level on a strong support. The wiring to the electrical equipment and heaters can be by PVC-sheathed three core flex secured at intervals to the greenhouse; there should be no trailing or loose cable or flex. With aluminium greenhouses you may have to drill small holes in the appropriate positions to allow buckle clips to be fixed with screws and nuts. In this case the PVC-sheathed cable will be in contact with metal and the greenhouse must be earthed by bolting an earth clamp to the frame and connecting a 6sq mm green/yellow PVC-insulated earth cable to this and to the earthing terminal of the main switch.

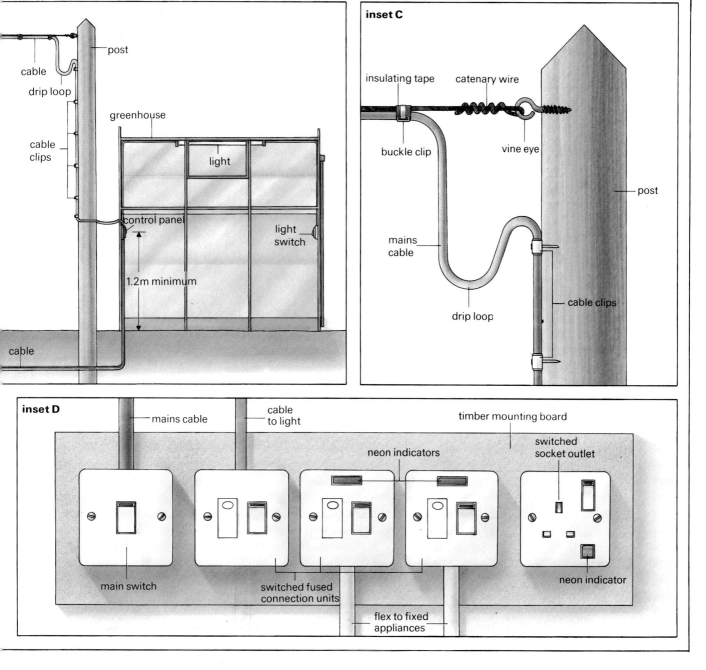

Diagnosing electrical faults

Fault	Cause	Remedy
Plug unduly hot	Loose flex terminal Fuse incorrectly fitted	Tighten terminal screws Ensure fuse makes contact over whole surface area of metal ends
	Poor quality fuse Fuse of incorrect rating	Fit BS 1362 ASTA Cert fuse Fit 13amp fuse if appliance rated at 750 watts or more
	Plug makes poor contact in socket Inferior quality plug Sustained load of 3kW causing reduced conductivity of pins and contacts	Renew plug and, if necessary, socket Fit plug of reliable make Renew plug
Sparks at socket outlet	Effect of breaking current in AC circuit If other than when operating switch, loose wire or faulty switch or socket	No action – natural phenomenon Tighten terminals, replace switch or socket
Intermittent power	Loose terminal or fuse or broken conductor	Tighten terminals and refit plug fuse; if only one appliance affected, check flex terminals in appliance
	Severed flex wire	Replace flex
Smell of burning in and around house	Old wiring or frayed flex; loose connection; insulation of wires in heater or other appliance touching hot parts of heater	Tighten terminals and replace damaged flexes and damaged exposed cables
	Lamp of too high wattage in enclosed light fitting or shade	Fit lamp of lower wattage
	Electric motor windings of powered appliance burning out, possibly due to blockage	Check and clear mechanical parts of appliance; otherwise call in electrician
Smell of burning near meter and consumer unit	Cable overheating between consumer unit and Board's service fuse unit. Circuit fuse wire in consumer unit hot and burning plastic before blowing. Loose connection. Fault in Board's terminal box, fuse holder or meter cables	Call Board's emergency service; any fault in this area will almost certainly require withdrawal of Board's service fuse which consumer must not touch
Fuse blows repeatedly without obvious cause	Cable or accessory fault; serious overloading; fuse of incorrect rating; faulty light fitting or appliance; TV suppressor faulty	Reduce load on circuit; fit fuse of correct rating; if circuit fuse, disconnect each appliance in turn to ascertain which causes fuse to blow
Intermittent switch or lamp failure; constant need for lamp replacement	Damaged or worn switch Faulty wiring or loose switch connection Lamp of wrong voltage Lamp burning in cap-down position	Replace switch Check wiring and connections Fit long life lamp of correct voltage Replace fitting with one which has lamp burning in cap-up position – could lengthen lamp life
	Mains voltage fluctuation due to nearby substation or mains tester	Ask Board to fit recording voltmeter
Loose switch	Age and wear	If switch body affected, replace switch; if loose in box, tighten fixing screws
Interference on hi-fi, TV or radio	If recent, faulty suppressor on appliance or new appliance has no suppressor Faulty thermostat Faulty fluorescent tube Faulty dimmer switch	Check each motor driven appliance; replace faulty suppressor Check each thermostat; replace if necessary Replace starter switch Fit new (suppressed) dimmer switch
No light or power	Mains switch accidentally turned off Board's fuse blown; supply failure or power cut	Check mains switch Check power available in neighbouring houses; if so, call Board